BULLYING
IN A CYBER WORLD

Reading, Writing, Discussing, Role-Playing, and More

Order Number 211338
ISBN 978-1-58324-353-4

A B C D E 16 15 14 13 12

The Association of Educational Publishers

395 Main Street
Rowley, MA 01969
www.didax.com

Foreword

Bullying is not a recent phenomenon; it has always been with us. The negative effects of childhood bullying can remain with both the bully and his or her targets long into adulthood. Everyone, child or adult, should be free to live without the fear of emotional abuse that bullying engenders.

Bullying in a Cyber World (Grades 6–8) gives insight into the many facets of bullying, providing material to help students understand why bullying is wrong and that, collectively, they have the power to eliminate it.

Bullying in a Cyber World is a complementary resource to the previously released Didax series, *Bullying: Identify, Cope, Prevent.*

Titles in this series are:

Bullying in a Cyber World (Grades 4–5)
Bullying in a Cyber World (Grades 6–8)

This series of books is supported by a set of six posters:

- *Bullying in a Cyber World*

Contents

The books in the series are divided into eight sections, each covering a particular aspect of bullying. In each section are two or three individual units, each with student pages and supporting teacher pages.

Teacher Pages

Each teacher page includes the following sections.

A **focus**, identifying the main purpose of the activity

Teacher information, providing background information relating to the topic

An **introduction**, with specific information and/or suggestions relating to the activity

Discussing the text, suggesting questions to promote discussion about the topic. Possible answers are included where appropriate.

Answers as necessary, to specific questions on student pages

Supporting activity/activities to develop the theme

Student Pages

The student pages are divided into three parts:

Read About It – A stimulus text to inform students about the theme and to promote discussion

Write About It – In which students demonstrate what they have learned about the theme from the stimulus text

More About It – An opportunity for students to think more deeply about the theme and how it relates to their own lives

These parts may be included on **one page** or on **three different pages**.

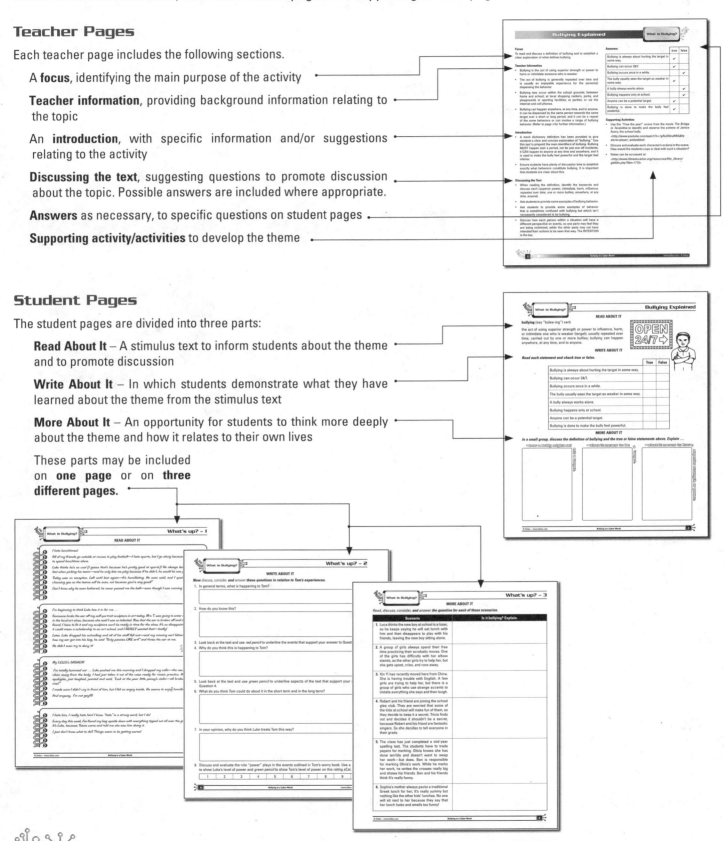

The eight sections are:

What Is Bullying? pages 2–9

Bullying is the act of using superior strength or power to intentionally harm, intimidate, or humiliate someone who is weaker.

The act of bullying is generally repeated over time and is usually an enjoyable experience for the person(s) dispensing the behavior.

An imbalance of power, whether real or perceived, is usually a key component of bullying. When one or more people feel they are more powerful than another, bullying situations and experiences may well develop and continue indefinitely. "Perceived power" imbalances may include: intellectual, social, physical, verbal, or financial.

Bullying may occur within the school grounds; between home and school; at local shopping centers, parks, and playgrounds, or sporting facilities; at parties; or via the Internet and cell phones.

Bullying can happen anywhere, at any time, and to anyone. It can be directed by the same person towards the same target over a short or long period, and it can be a repeat of the same behaviors or can involve a range of bullying behaviors.

In order to identify bullying behaviors and tactics, we first need to identify behaviors that are sometimes misinterpreted as bullying. The first is mutual conflict between two students over a problem. In this type of situation, both parties generally want a fair resolution but are having difficulty reaching one, and there is a balance of power. The second situation involves social rejection or dislike. We don't always have to like everyone, as long as we respect each person for who he or she is. Some children may feel they are being bullied just because someone doesn't particularly like spending time with them. This does not constitute bullying behavior. The third situation is when ugliness occurs on a single occasion. A child may push another child on the playground on a particular day. Unless physical, verbal, or psychological acts occur on several occasions, this is not considered bullying either.

Forms of Bullying, pages 10–21

Although the vast amount of research currently available categorizes bullying in varying ways, the content remains consistent.

Bullying, which can occur between an individual or a group of bullies and an individual or a group of targets, can broadly be categorized as physical, social, or psychological. The resilience of the target and the extent of the bullying are key factors in determining how severely the target is affected emotionally. Depending on the circumstances, bullying acts can occur in any of the following categories.

Physical bullying is direct contact between the bully and the target. Examples include verbal abuse relating to the target's appearance, family, home, possessions, physical, and intellectual abilities; punching, kicking, and tripping; using or throwing objects to cause personal injury; intimidation that threatens physical abuse; extortion in which money or goods are demanded to avoid physical injury to the target or his or her family; deliberate damage to the target's property or something borrowed in his or her name, and theft of a target's possessions or those borrowed in his or her name.

Social bullying is any actions on the part of the bully that make the target feel humiliated or embarrassed in front of his or her peers or excluded by them. Examples can include being excluded from conversations, jokes, games, peer groups, social activities; being mocked and mimicked for intellectual and athletic capabilities, physical appearance, and habits; being the object of unkind messages sent to others via gestures, notes, texting, e-mails; talking negatively about something related to the target, pretending the target is not within earshot; making silent phone calls or sending cryptic text messages; and being "befriended" by the bullies and asked to do foolish things "as a joke." The target is then ridiculed for his or her foolish actions.

Psychological bullying is a form of bullying that can be difficult for the target to prove, so he or she is less likely to report it. The bully can appear totally innocent of any wrongdoing, but he or she has a powerful negative hold over the target. Examples can include following or stalking, silently threatening intent to harm; gestures such as wafting a hand over the nose when the target approaches, implying that he or she has a personal hygiene problem; and subtle exclusion, such as greeting everyone else with a smile and eye contact but ignoring the target.

Cyberbullying, pages 22–33

Cyberbullying is the act of bullying a target using technology such as cell phones or the Internet as a vehicle.

In the real world there are generally physical boundaries where the bullying stops; for example, at home or in the classroom (with the teacher present). However, cyberspace knows no boundaries and a target has no reprieve or safe haven from his or her tormentor.

Cyberbullying includes repeated attacks, threats, defamation, or harassment designed to cause distress to the chosen target. The bully or group of bullies may use cell-phone messages or pictures, Internet social sites or blogs, or e-mail to render the torment. They may stage the same attack over and over or vary the delivery. It may be organized by one bully and carried out by several others, or it may be organized and carried out by the same person.

Cyberspace provides the bully with a sense of anonymity that they can't possibly have in the physical world. It allows them to take the bullying to another level beyond what is possible at school or other traditional bullying hot spots. It also provides the target with a hard copy of the event(s), which they are then able to read and reread many times over—causing much deeper harm.

Traditional bullying may be observed by a few people or a large group of ten or more. However, technology allows the bullying to be witnessed (and carried on) by a far greater audience—adding to the target's humiliation.

This form of bullying can also be continued over a longer period, and total strangers can join in. Almost like a ripple in a pond, it can grow and grow. Every time someone forwards a text message or e-mail, that person helps the bully to continue his or her campaign against the target.

Fortunately, this technology also provides a level of security that cannot be found in real life. Education and an understanding of the technology will provide a safe and secure environment. Individuals have the ability to lock their profile, blog, or webpage—allowing only selected friends access to their information, while specific callers can be blocked from cell phone contact lists.

Individuals also need to be aware of the information they share with others. It is up to the individual to carefully consider the sharing of photographs, information, and personal events. By taking simple precautions, individuals can take charge and reduce the risk of becoming an online target.

The "upside" of cyberbullying, if there is one, is that it does provide a hard copy that can be saved and used as evidence against the bully. The target must be educated to save and keep all documentation and share it with the appropriate authorities (school, parent, law enforcement officers) to have the matter dealt with. Criminal legislation is now available to pursue any specific behaviors involving the use of such technology to cause harm to another person.

Types of Cyberbullying

Cyberstalking occurs when an individual repeatedly sends threatening messages via the Internet or a cell phone. The messages instill the fear that the stalking might move offline and become physical.

Flaming involves sending correspondence using chat rooms, e-mail, and instant messenger. Flaming refers to arguments to which images are often added to emphasize a point. It includes harsh language.

Exclusion occurs when an individual is singled out and excluded from a group. The group then taunts the excluded person using the Internet or cell phones.

Outing occurs when an individual publicly shares personal communications involving another person using online communication methods or a cell phone. That individual is then "outed" when his/her private information is broadcast publicly, either online or offline.

Masquerading is a form of cyberbullying in which an individual creates a false identity and harasses another while pretending to be someone else. Masquerading includes attempts to steal log-in information and then using that information in a harassing manner, such as sharing it publicly.

Impersonation is pretending to be someone else and sending or posting material online to make the impersonated person look bad, get him/her in trouble or danger, or cause damage to that person's reputation or friendships.

Harassment is the act of repeatedly sending offensive, rude, or insulting messages.

Denigration is the act of ridiculing someone online. It involves sending or posting cruel gossip or rumors about a person to damage his or her reputation or friendships.

Targets of Bullying, pages 34–41

Anyone can be bullied. It may be for a specific reason or for no particular reason. Bullies enjoy the sense of power they have over their targets and they thrive on the reactions elicited from them. A target who gets upset, showing fear or anger, is more likely to be ruthlessly pursued by a bully, whereas one who ignores a bully's taunts may be left alone. Often, a person (or group of people) is singled out for bullying because they are different in some way from the mainstream group. This difference puts them in the minority. As the motivating force behind bullying is power, targeting a minority group is an easy option for the cowardly bully.

Minority groups commonly targeted by bullies are those of different ...

- **Race** – with different-colored skin, hair type, or facial features

- **Religion** – who follow a different (or any) religious faith

- **Culture** – from another region or country and who may have different accents, languages, foods, fashions, and customs

- **Sexual orientation** – those who are gay or who are perceived to be gay because of their choice of style, fashion, activities, or friends. A person can become a bully's target if a family member of the target is gay or if his or her family unit comprises same-sex parents. Bullying of this nature is known as homophobic bullying.

- **Physical ability** – This can be divided into two main groups: those who have a medically recognized physical disability, including those who wear hearing aids and glasses, and those who have all their faculties but are not adept at either fine or gross motor skills. The latter are often bullied for their lack of sporting prowess.

- **Intellectual ability** – This can also be divided into two main groups: those who have a medically recognized intellectual disability and those who have all their faculties but who are at either end of the curve of natural distribution. If a nonacademic student is talented in another area, he or she may escape bullying. Academically gifted students are often bullied, and some deliberately underachieve in order to fit in with the majority.

- **Physical features** – In addition to those who may be bullied because of different physical features related to race, some become targets because they have features that do not match the norm. Examples include big ears, lower than average height, unruly hair, prominent birthmarks, and protruding teeth.

- **Social status** – This is manifest in many areas, such as type of home, car, suburb, lower or higher than average family income, personal possessions (whether or not the target has the latest electronic toys and gadgets), and types of vacations and social activities.

- **Personality** – Shy students are often targeted by bullies. They lack the confidence to stand up to the bully and find it difficult to tell someone about the problem. Their vulnerability often prolongs the bullying onslaught, and they may retreat even further into their shells.

Effects of Bullying, pages 42–47

All targets are affected to some degree by bullying, but the extent depends on their confidence, self-esteem, and resilience. Some will have strategies for coping with the bullying, thus ending the problem, but many more will suffer consequences in the short and long term.

Some short-term consequences ...

- For the *target* are: loss of appetite; insomnia; feelings of sadness, fear, anger, shame, loneliness; excessive absenteeism from school; drop in schoolwork standards; poor attention span; loss of interest in social activities; anxiety attacks; feeling responsible for the attacks; lack of trust in friends.

- For the *bully* are: shallow friendships (peers are "friends" for fear of being bullied themselves); negative reputation among school personnel and some students.

Some long-term consequences ...

- For the *target* are: low self-esteem; difficulty in making and maintaining friendships; depression; nonfulfillment of academic potential; poor career prospects; open to bullying in the workplace; paranoia—specifically related to cyberbullying; self-harm; possible suicide; revenge attacks; and abusive behavior at home.

- For the *bully* are: unpopularity and loss of peer group as "friends" no longer fear retribution; continued antisocial behavior possibly leading to crime; and abusive behavior at home.

Who Bullies and Why? pages 48–59

Although the focus in schools is often on providing support for the targets of bullying, the bullies themselves also need to be understood so they too can be helped.

Categories of Bullies

- **Bystander bullies:** Even bystanders who observe bullying and take no active role in that bullying are themselves classified as bullies if they fail to take any action.

- **Accessory bullies:** Bystanders become accessories to bullying when they encourage a bully by, for example, making statements of support, laughing, jeering, or mimicking.

- **Advocates:** There is a further category involved in bullying: those who are neither targets nor bullies. They haven't actually observed the bullying, but they may suspect that bullying is occurring. This group can be very effective in preventing bullying.

Bystander bullying is of particular relevance in cyberbullying. Students may pass on images or information that amuses or shocks them. They may do this without thinking of, or being aware of, the effect on the target or of their own role as a bully. Depending on the nature of the material being sent, these students could be performing an illegal act.

Characteristics of Bullies

The following list contains generalizations about bullies. There can be no one set of characteristics to describe all bullies. A bully may be a very confident, high-achieving, apparently popular student with high self-esteem or a target who is retaliating by bullying other less powerful or younger students in order to hide his or her own lack of confidence. Bullying is about power and control.

Bullies may have a conduct disorder; lack empathy and sympathy; be confident and popular; lack self-esteem, and have difficulty making friends; be physically bigger and stronger than their victims; be able to talk their way out of trouble; have a small group of friends who support their bullying; question authority, break rules, push boundaries, and admire violence; tend towards physical bullying if they are boys, or be more likely to use social exclusion or humiliation if they are girls; be impulsive, socially dominant, easily frustrated, confrontational, aggressive, needing to control, or attention-seeking.

There is no common reason for bullying, but the following generalizations worthy of consideration are: jealousy and competition for attention and valued objects; personal experience of being bullied; inadequate supervision; child abuse and neglect; harsh physical discipline; overly permissive parenting or lack of limits; inconsistent enforcement of rules and consequences; or poor role models at home or school.

Students have reported they have bullied others because: "They are annoying"; "To get even"; "It's fun"; "To take things I want from others"; "Others do it"; "To show how tough I am"; "They're weak"; "They deserve it"; or "I can."

Dealing with Bullying, pages 60–69

To persist with bullying, bullies rely on evoking a reaction from their targets. They want to see fear, hurt, or anger. These responses give bullies the feeling of power on which they thrive. By learning strategies to deal positively with bullying attacks, students are empowered to stand up for themselves and are less likely to be regular targets in the future.

Examples of strategies to give students include:

- *Have a ready response for a given bullying situation and deliver it with direct eye contact with the bully before walking away confidently.* Examples of these responses can be practiced during role-play of prevalent bullying situations. It takes courage for students to appear brave while inside they may be feeling quite the opposite, especially if they are on their own against more than one assailant. But by reacting in this way, they are challenging the bully, who in many cases will back down, since most bullies are cowards.

- *Do not react emotionally to the bully but look him or her straight in the eye before smiling and carrying on with the activity in progress.* This action says, "You can't hurt me, and I'm not bothered by what you say or do." Bullies do not like to be ignored, so if the student can calmly play out this response, the bully will get the message.

- *Turn what the bully says or does into a joke.* Without making fun of the bully, if a target can make light of the situation, the bully will see that he/she has no power over the target.

- *Improve your body language.* By walking purposefully with shoulders back and head held high, students will look less vulnerable, reducing the likelihood of being targeted.

- *Increase your social circle.* By making an effort to engage fellow students in general conversation and showing an interest in them and their lives, students develop a greater social network and potential support against bullying.

- *Talk to people if you feel you are being bullied.* In sharing their experiences, students realize they are not alone, and they can identify peers and adults in whom they can confide. They will need to know that in talking with school staff, their problems will be taken seriously and dealt with appropriately. If more than one student is being targeted by the same bully or group of bullies, they can go together to speak to a staff member. The sooner the target talks about the problem, the sooner it can be dealt with and the risk of emotional damage reduced.

- *Keep any evidence of bullying.* A record of events with names of bystanders and witnesses is useful for recalling details. Any physical evidence related to the bullying, such as a note that has been passed around, should be retained. While cyberbullying is difficult to trace and monitor, saving all messages and e-mails will help in tracking down the initial perpetrator. Instruct students to inform an adult as soon as they receive any unwanted photos, texts, or e-mails, and if they discover anything negative relating to them on social networking sites. Students need to talk to their parents and trusted friends about being bullied in this way. It is one type of bullying from which it is almost impossible to escape, so it is important that they have a supportive network in whom they can confide and discuss the content of the photos and/or messages.

- *If possible, avoid the bully.* While no one should have to use avoidance tactics to be safe, it is possible that keeping out of the bully's way for a while may be enough to stop the opportunistic bully who has no specific gripe against the target but who bullies just because he or she can. In more serious cases, adults should be informed of unsafe areas where bullies are likely to strike.

- *Avoid being alone when you are at risk of being bullied.* It is not always possible to avoid bullies. In those cases, students should make every effort to be in the company of their friends.

- *Know where the "safe houses" are on your route home.* If a bully saves his intimidation for after school, it is helpful for students to know if there is a place of safety between school and home.

- *Walk to and from school with friends.* Students should feel safe to walk to and from school alone without harassment, but if they are concerned, walking with friends will ease their discomfort.

Walk confidently with shoulders back and head held high. Lose your frown, and your fears and worries will go, too. Look and feel happier with a smile.

Preventing Bullying, pages 70–81

Bullying is not a new problem or one that all teachers see the same need to deal with—some perhaps because they perceive bullying as "just a part of growing up" and as something they and others have all survived. Others may believe the problem of bullying is too difficult and believe they lack the skills and training to deal with it effectively. But preventing bullying, particularly at a time when cyberbullying is affecting an increasing number of students, is important, and there is a great deal teachers and the students in their classes can and must do to protect targets from pain and humiliation.

Teachers need to:

- Participate in whole-school planning to deal with bullying ... and include students in this planning.
- Ensure that students and parents understand the school bullying policy.
- Be consistent in imposing consequences for bullying behaviors.
- Help students to accept and appreciate physical, cultural, and attitudinal differences.
- Listen, try to understand, and respond appropriately to reported bullying behaviors.
- Be sensitive to the needs of both targets and bullies.
- Ensure that all students are well informed about different forms of bullying and how to deal with them.
- Provide opportunities for students to understand bullying and empathize through role-plays and discussions.
- Realize how effective well-informed advocates (students who are neither bullies nor victims) can be in preventing bullying.
- Be informed about the different forms, possibilities, and technologies involved in cyberbullying.
- Realize cyberbullying between students at home needs to be addressed by parents and the school.

All students need to:

- Be able to identify bullying, and differentiate between bullying and hurtful behaviors that are isolated or unintentional.
- Be involved in the development of the school's bullying policy.
- Empathize with targets and understand more about bullying through discussions and role-plays.
- Appreciate differences in cultural practices, values, physical appearance, abilities, and attitudes, including sexual orientation.
- Accept that they have a role in supporting targets and preventing bullying.
- Understand that it is acceptable to report bullying.
- Understand that some forms of cyberbullying are illegal.
- Be aware of the need to protect personal details when posting information in chat rooms and on networking sites.

Targets need to:

- Be able to identify bullying behaviors and realize that bullying is wrong.
- Understand that it is acceptable to report bullying.
- Know they will be listened to and that action will be taken when they report bullying.
- Realize they are not alone and that other students understand and will help them.
- Have strategies to employ when bullied (things they can do or say).
- Keep any evidence of cyberbullying.
- Develop a support network.

Preventing Bullying, pages 70–81 (continued)

Bullies need to:

- Realize that bullying is wrong.
- Understand when they are bullying.
- Expect that bullying will be reported.
- Realize there are consistently applied consequences of bullying and that it will not be tolerated.
- Learn to empathize more with the feelings of others.
- Become more tolerant and less aggressive.
- Learn to interact with others and resolve differences in a more acceptable way.
- Understand that posting photos and hurtful or false information is a form of bullying.

Accessories or bystanders who are also bullies because they actively support bullies need to:

- Realize if they support or encourage a bully by joining in, passing on hurtful material, or even laughing, they are accessories and therefore are bullies, too.
- Know they have choices and do not have to support bullying.
- Know others will help them if they, too, become a target.
- Understand that it is acceptable to report bullying.

Bystanders who are also bullies because they passively support bullies by doing nothing need to:

- Realize that by not supporting the target, they are being bullies, too.

Advocates who are neither bullies nor targets need to:

- Realize the importance of their role in preventing bullying.
- Learn strategies to deal with bullies and victims.
- Report bullying.

BULLYING IN SCHOOLS

It is now widely accepted that bullying is unacceptable at any level and that everyone has the right to a bully-free life at school and in the outside world.

A Safe School Environment

The school environment itself should discourage bullying activities. Staff supervision on the playground, in school buildings, and on buses should create safe areas for play, and retreat and eliminate "blind spots" where bullying may occur. The physical design of the school buildings may also need to be considered. Schools need to target key times and locations for bullying and take steps to minimize risks to potential targets. Students may assist in providing this information.

Professional Development

In order for schools to effectively combat bullying, staff and other adult helpers or supervisors need to understand bullying fully. Professional development by experts should include information about legal responsibilities relating to the care of students at school. A number of states have anti-bullying laws, and the federal government offers an anti-bullying resource kit at <www.stopbullyingnow.hrsa.gov>.

Establishing an Anti-Bullying Policy

A school needs to assure its students that bullying will not be tolerated, incidents will be thoroughly investigated, perpetrators will be dealt with appropriately, and targets will be supported. The biggest hurdle to achieving a bullying-free school is that many incidents go unreported, either because targets and witnesses fear retribution, or because they believe that although an initial investigation may take place, there will be no follow-up and the bullying will be allowed to continue.

Establishing an Anti-Bullying Policy (continued)

While an anti-bullying plan is being drawn up by the school, involving students in the process will help them feel "ownership" of the document. Ensure that students know the policy and all procedures, including the consequences. They will be more likely to report bullying incidents if they are familiar with the policy and believe the procedures will be followed.

Students, parents, and staff provide valuable information regarding their personal experiences of bullying. This will help the school establish, and evaluate the effectiveness of, the anti-bullying policy.

When establishing an anti-bullying policy, the school leadership team should actively demonstrate positive anti-bullying behaviors and, if possible, gain support from the wider community, especially parents. Other schools in the local area may also be interested in working together to establish an anti-bullying policy.

Recording of bullying incidents should be clear and consistent. Confidentiality, fair and effective investigations, listening strategies, and appropriate follow-up should all be included in a bullying policy.

Consequences for bullies should be fair, consistent, and reasonable. The bully should be provided with opportunities to learn from and change the offending behavior.

Victims should be supported—disruption to normal routines should be kept to a minimum and they should be aware that the bully is being dealt with.

Rewards for students taking care of each other and good behavior should be well established. By engaging in role-play, students should know how to support each other and assert themselves in a bullying situation. By building confidence and resilience, students should be able to better withstand bullying.

Including Anti-Bullying Messages in Other Learning Areas

Curriculum areas provide opportunities to raise awareness of bullying. Physical education and character education lessons can be used to discuss issues and support anti-bullying procedures. Creative activities such as music, drama, and art can develop positive social and emotional aspects.

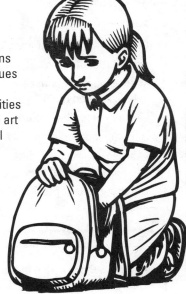

Name: _____ Date: _____

Who was involved?

(blank box)

Describe the incident. Include:

- What happened
- Exactly what you did
- Why you think it happened
- What you saw the others do
- Why you were there

(blank box)

Who do you think was/were the target/targets, bully/bullies, and bystander/bystanders in this incident?

Target/Targets	Bully/Bullies	Bystander/Bystanders

Student's signature: _____ Class teacher's signature: _____

Bullying Incident Report

Teacher completing form: _____ Date: _____

Student reporting incident: _____ Class: _____

Students involved and their roles—target/bully/bystander

Incident details

Date: _____ *Time:* _____ *Location:* _____

Steps taken to resolve incident

Follow-up interview date _____

Parents informed?   *No* ☐   *Yes* ☐   *Date:* _____

Teacher's signature: _____   Class teacher's signature: _____

School: _____   Class: _____

> **We believe that everyone has the right to feel safe and happy at school.**
> **No one has the right to threaten, humiliate, or exclude another.**
> **We want to stamp out bullying in our school.**
> **We believe that together we have the power to achieve this goal.**

As we sign this pledge, we agree to:

❖ Value the inner person and not the outward appearance

❖ Celebrate and respect our talents and differences

❖ Make everyone feel welcome

❖ Take no part in bullying

❖ Report all bullying incidents

❖ Support all targets of bullying

❖ Help bullies understand that their behavior is unacceptable.

_____   _____   _____

_____   _____   _____

_____   _____   _____

_____   _____   _____

_____   _____   _____

_____   _____   _____

_____   _____   _____

_____   _____   _____

Class teacher: _____   Date: _____

Anti-Bullying Pledge

I believe that everyone has the right to feel safe and happy at school.
No one has the right to threaten, humiliate, or exclude another.
I want to help to stamp out bullying in our school.
I believe that together we have the power to achieve this goal.

In signing this pledge, I agree to:

❖ Value the inner person and not the outward appearance
❖ Celebrate and respect our talents and differences
❖ Make everyone feel welcome
❖ Take no part in bullying
❖ Report all bullying incidents
❖ Support all targets of bullying.
❖ Help bullies understand that their behavior is unacceptable.

Student's name: _____ Class: _____

Teacher: _____ Date: _____

Anti-Bullying Pledge

We believe that everyone has the right to feel safe and happy at school.
No one has the right to threaten, humiliate, or exclude another.
We want to help to stamp out bullying in our school.
We believe that together we have the power to achieve this goal.

In signing this pledge, we agree to:

❖ Foster positive attitudes towards all people
❖ Welcome everyone to our community
❖ Work out positive ways to solve problems
❖ Celebrate and respect our talents and differences
❖ Support all targets of bullying
❖ Help bullies understand that their behavior is unacceptable.

Student: _____ Class: _____

Parents: _____ Date: _____

Teacher: _____ Date: _____

 awarded to

.... for

Speaking Out Against Bullying

by ....

....

Teacher: .... Date: ....

    awarded to

.... for

Showing Support for Peers

by ....

....

Teacher: .... Date: ....

Say No to B u l l y i n g

Bullying in a Cyber World

Internet Safety Checklist

When online I will ...   Name _____

- ❖ Create a clever password and keep it private. ☐

- ❖ Always log out of shared computers. ☐

- ❖ Never give out my full name, address, phone number, birthday, school, or club names. ☐

- ❖ Communicate respectfully with others. ☐

- ❖ Never arrange a face-to-face meeting with a stranger. ☐

- ❖ Only download from known or trusted websites. ☐

- ❖ Tell a trusted adult if I see something that makes me feel uncomfortable. ☐

- ❖ Never open e-mails from people I don't know. ☐

- ❖ Seek permission before sharing pictures or information about other people online. ☐

Cyber Safety Checklist

Parent

To ensure my child is protected online, I will ...   Name _____

- ❖ Educate myself about dangers he/she may encounter, including online predators and cyberbullying. ☐

- ❖ Talk to my child about things on the Web that make him/her feel uncomfortable. ☐

- ❖ Monitor his/her Internet use by sharing an e-mail account, checking browser history, keeping the computer in a shared location, and maintaining access to my child's account. ☐

- ❖ Research and recommend appropriate child-safe sites. ☐

- ❖ Maintain an appropriate amount of parental control of software through user time limits and access to sites, games, chat, and file sharing. ☐

- ❖ Install defensive software such as anti-virus, anti-spyware, spam blocker, and personal firewall, and update these regularly. ☐

- ❖ Select child-safe mobile devices, including those that do not include a camera or web access, and phones with a limit on the number of calls that can be made. ☐

Internet Resources

There are many Internet sites that give information on how to recognize and deal with bullying. For example:

Cyber Bullying Research Center: *http://www.cyberbullying.us/resources.php*

Education.com: Bullying at School and Online: *http://www.education.com/topic/school-bullying-teasing/*

Education.com: Cyberbullying Resources: *http://www.education.com/reference/article/cyberbullying-resources/*

EducationWorld.com: Special Theme: Bullying: *http://www.educationworld.com/a_special/bully.shtml*

Health Resources and Services Administration: Stop Bullying Now! *http://www.stopbullyingnow.hrsa.gov/kids/*

National Crime Prevention Council: Cyberbullying: *http://www.ncpc.org/cyberbullying*

Books

Bullying: Identify, Cope, Prevent
by Didax Education

Conflict Resolution (Grades 6–8)
by Didax Education

Blubber
by Judy Blume

Bystander
by James Preller

End Game
by Nancy Garden

Half Mast
by Christopher Null

Hate List
by Jennifer Brown

Poison Ivy
by Amy Goldman Koss

Scrawl
by Mark Shulman

Don't Call Me Ishmael!
by Michael Gerard Bauer

Feather Wars
by Sally Grindley

The Mighty Crashman
by Jerry Spinelli

The Savage
by David Almond
illustrated by Dave McKean

Who the Man
by Chris Lynch

Now
by Morris Gleitzman

Racing the Past
by Sis Deans

Josie Under Fire
by Ann Turnbull

Missing Abby
by Lee Weatherly

Weirdo's War
by Michael Coleman

For Parents and Teachers

The Bully, the Bullied, and the Bystander: From Preschool to High School—How Parents and Teachers Can Help Break the Cycle
by Barbara Coloroso

Bullying Beyond the Schoolyard: Preventing and Responding to Cyberbullying
by Sameer Hinduja and Justin W. Patchin

Schools Where Everyone Belongs: Practical Strategies for Reducing Bullying
by Stan Davis

Focus

To read and discuss a definition of bullying and to establish a clear explanation of what defines bullying

Teacher Information

- Bullying is the act of using superior strength or power to harm or intimidate someone who is weaker.

- The act of bullying is generally repeated over time and is usually an enjoyable experience for the person(s) dispensing the behavior.

- Bullying may occur on the school grounds; between home and school; at local shopping centers, parks, and playgrounds or sporting facilities; at parties; or via the Internet and cell phones.

- Bullying can happen anywhere, at any time, and to anyone. It can be dispensed by the same person towards the same target over a short or long period, and it can be a repeat of the same behaviors or can involve a range of bullying behaviors. (Refer to page *v* for further information.)

Introduction

- A mock dictionary definition has been provided to give students a clear and concise explanation of "bullying." Use this text to pinpoint the main identifiers of bullying. Bullying MUST happen over a period of time, rather than being a one-off incident. It CAN happen to anyone at any time and anywhere, and it is used to make the bully feel powerful and the target feel inferior.

- Ensure students have plenty of discussion time to establish exactly what behaviors constitute bullying. It is important that students are clear about this.

Discussing the Text

- When reading the definition, identify the keywords and discuss each (*superior power, intimidate, harm, influence, repeated over time, one or more bullies, anywhere, at any time, anyone*).

- Ask students to provide some examples of bullying behavior.

- Ask students to provide some examples of behavior that is sometimes confused with bullying but isn't necessarily considered to be bullying.

- Discuss how each person in a situation will have a different perspective on events, so one party may feel they are being victimized, while the other party may not have intended their actions to be seen that way. The INTENTION is the key.

Answers	True	False
Bullying is always about hurting the target in some way.	✔	
Bullying can occur 24/7.	✔	
Bullying occurs once in a while.		✔
The bully usually sees the target as weaker in some way.	✔	
A bully always works alone.		✔
Bullying happens only at school.		✔
Anyone can be a potential target.	✔	
Bullying is done to make the bully feel powerful.	✔	

Supporting Activities

- Use the "Free the pee!" scene from the movie *The Bridge to Terabithia* to identify and observe the actions of Janice Avery, the school bully.

  <http://www.youtube.com/watch?v=1gRoQNvu8W A&feature=player_embedded>

- Discuss and evaluate each character's actions in the scene. How would the students cope or deal with such a situation?

- Notes can be accessed at:

  <http://www.filmeducation.org/resources/film_ library/getfilm.php?film=1715>

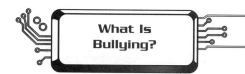

READ ABOUT IT

bullying (say "bŭlee-ing") verb

the act of using superior strength or power to influence, harm, or intimidate one who is weaker (target); usually repeated over time; carried out by one or more bullies; bullying can happen anywhere, at any time, and to anyone.

OPEN 24/7 →

WRITE ABOUT IT

Read each statement and check true or false.

	True	False
Bullying is always about hurting the target in some way.		
Bullying can occur 24/7.		
Bullying occurs once in a while.		
The bully usually sees the target as weaker in some way.		
A bully always works alone.		
Bullying happens only at school.		
Anyone can be a potential target.		
Bullying is done to make the bully feel powerful.		

MORE ABOUT IT

In a small group, discuss the definition of bullying and the true or false statements above. Explain …

○ **how a bully might**

select a target.

○ **what it means to**

be a target.

○ **what it means to**

have superior strength or power.

Focus

To observe a satirical cartoon image and read a paragraph in order to discuss and clearly outline the "role of power" in bullying situations

Teacher Information

- An imbalance of power, whether real or perceived, is usually a key component of bullying. When one or more people feel they are more powerful than another, bullying situations and experiences may well develop and continue indefinitely. "Perceived power" imbalances may be intellectual, social, physical, verbal, or financial. (Refer to page *v* for further information.)

Introduction

- An image has been used to demonstrate that the bully's "power" is not always obvious, but exists in the bully's mind. Therefore, it is not always easy to identify who might be a bully. The supporting text explicitly states the role "power" plays in bullying situations.

- The activity is asking students to reiterate the concept as clearly as possible to ensure a clear understanding of the role "power" plays in bullying situations. This clear understanding then leads to providing the opportunity for students to discuss and establish ways to counteract "power"!

Discussing the Text

- First, look at the image and ask students to tell you what they see. How does it make them feel? What is the picture trying to show? (The two boys are the same size, but in the mind of the bully, he is more powerful and dominates the scene; the target's body language is showing that the bully has power.)

- Can you always identify what it is that makes a particular bully "powerful"? Is it always clear? If so, then different approaches can be used to remove the power. What might these be? (It is important that students understand that you can't pick a bully out of a crowd based on how he or she looks.)

Answers

- The bully usually feels more POWERFUL in some way than his or her target.

- Power isn't just about SIZE; it can be about anything.

- A bully can be physically SMALLER than his or her target; however, the bully does consider himself/herself to be superior in some way.

- The more often the bully gets away with bullying behavior, the more SUPERIOR he or she will feel.

Supporting Activities

- Role-play various situations that allow students the opportunity to practice TAKING THE POWER AWAY FROM the bully.

- Chapter 5, "The Giant Killers," from *The Bridge to Terabithia* demonstrates how Leslie and Jess take away Janice's power. Have students observe what they do and discuss the appropriateness of this approach. Ask: What else could they have done?

READ ABOUT IT

"TARGET"   "BULLY"

Bullying usually occurs when one person considers himself or herself to be superior to or more powerful than another person in some way. It's not always about size or physical strength; sometimes it can be about intelligence, ability, friendship groups, cultural or physical differences, wealth, or interests.

WRITE ABOUT IT

Use the image and text, together with discussion, to complete these sentences.

size	superior	powerful	smaller

The bully usually feels more _____ in some way than his or her target.

Power isn't just about _____; it can be about anything.

A bully can be physically _____ than his or her target; however, he or she does consider himself/herself to be superior in some way.

The more often the bully gets away with bullying behavior, the more _____ he or she will feel.

MORE ABOUT IT

In a small group, discuss the image above.

Use this discussion to devise an approach that could be used to remove the "power" from the bully. Draw the steps below and then present a short role-play to the class to demonstrate your techniques.

_____   _____   _____
_____   _____   _____

Focus

To read and discuss extracts from Tom's worry book, which will help to clarify and identify episodes of behavior that are considered to be bullying and those that are not

Teacher Information

- In order to identify bullying behaviors and tactics, we first need to identify behaviors that are sometimes misinterpreted as bullying. The first is mutual conflict between two students over a problem. In this type of situation, both parties generally want a fair resolution but are having difficulty reaching one, and there is a balance of power. The second situation involves social rejection or dislike. We don't always have to like everyone, so long as we respect people for who they are. Some children may feel they are being bullied just because someone doesn't particularly like spending time with them. This does not constitute bullying behavior. The third situation is when ugliness occurs on a single occasion. A child may push another child on the playground on a particular day. Unless physical, verbal, or psychological acts occur on several occasions, this is not considered bullying either. (Refer to page *v* for information.)

Introduction

- The text provided is designed to demonstrate how bullying can sometimes escalate. The bully, Luke, didn't necessarily start out to bully Tom, but as time passes and he gets a reaction from Tom, Luke's behavior escalates and becomes bullying. Luke begins to see that he has "power" over Tom.

- Students must be given ample opportunity to reread, discuss the text, and share their ideas and opinions on what they have read and how it has made them feel.

- The activities are designed to encourage students to look at the text objectively and to find supporting evidence there to back up their thoughts and ideas.

- The final page gives students the opportunity to clearly identify bullying behavior as opposed to one's perception of events or even behavior that may not be very nice but is not considered to be bullying.

Discussing the Text

- There are several underlying tones within the text. What are they? (Tom is not athletic but artistic; Luke perceives these talents as "gay"; Tom is doing his best to fit in so as not to be isolated; Luke develops a taste for "power.")

- How does Tom's behavior contribute to the bullying episodes? (He doesn't stand up for himself, which gives Luke the power in each situation; he shows that Luke's behavior upsets him.)

- What is Teena's role in the last entry? What could she have done? (Teena is a bystander; she could have intervened and told Luke to leave Tom's bag alone.)

- Why is Luke targeting Tom? What is the pay-off for him? (Luke is targeting Tom because it gives him power; Tom's response gives Luke what he needs.)

- How could Tom turn the situation around? (Tom needs to be assertive and also get an adult involved in the situation before it becomes more serious.)

Answers

Page 8

1. Tom is being bullied.
2. The bullying behaviors are repeated, harmful, and enjoyable to Luke.
3. Teacher check
4. Tom is different and creative, rather than a "physical" person.

5–8. Teacher check

Page 9

Teacher check

Supporting Activities

- Role-play Tom standing up to Luke. What might he say? What might Luke's reaction be? By standing up to Luke, how will Tom feel?

- Discuss the various scenarios the students role-played and decide which might be the most effective strategies.

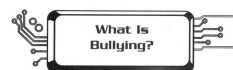
READ ABOUT IT

I hate lunchtimes!

All of my friends go outside at recess to play football—I hate sports, but I go along because I don't want to spend lunchtime alone.

Luke thinks he's so cool (I guess that's because he's pretty good at sports)! He always leaves me until last when picking his team—and he only lets me play because if he didn't, he would be one person short.

Today was no exception. Left until last again—it's humiliating. He even said, and I quote: "Tom, I'm only choosing you so the teams will be even, not because you're any good!"

Don't know why he even bothered, he never passed me the ball—even though I was running my guts out!

I'm beginning to think Luke has it in for me …

Someone broke the ear off my self-portrait sculpture in art today. Mrs T. was going to enter my sculpture in the local art show, because she said I was so talented. Now that the ear is broken off and nowhere to be found, I have to fix it and my sculpture won't be ready in time for the show. It's so disappointing, because it could mean a scholarship to art school, and I REALLY wanted that—badly!

Later, Luke dropped his backpack and all of his stuff fell out—and my missing ear! When I asked him how my ear got into his backpack, he said "Only pansies LIKE art!" and threw the ear at me.

He didn't even try to deny it!

My CELLO's BROKEN!

I'm totally bummed out … Luke pushed me this morning, and I dropped my cello—the neck has broken clean away from the body. I had just taken it out of the case ready for music practice. He didn't even apologize, just laughed, pointed, and said, "Look at the poor little pansy's violin—all broken—don't cry now!"

I made sure I didn't cry in front of him, but I felt so angry inside. He seems to enjoy humiliating me!

And anyway, I'm not gay!!!!

I hate him, I really hate him! I know "hate" is a strong word, but I do!

Every day this week, I've found my backpack upside down with everything dumped out on the ground! I know it's Luke, because Tina came and told me she saw him doing it.

I just don't know what to do!! Things seem to be getting worse!

WRITE ABOUT IT

Now discuss, consider, *and* answer *these questions in relation to Tom's experiences.*

1. In general terms, what is happening to Tom?

2. How do you know this?

3. Look back at the text and use *red pencil* to underline the events that support your answer to Question 2.

4. Why do you think this is happening to Tom?

5. Look back at the text and use *green pencil* to underline aspects of the text that support your answer to Question 4.

6. What do you think Tom could do about it in the short term and in the long term?

7. In your opinion, why do you think Luke treats Tom this way?

8. Discuss and evaluate the role "power" plays in the events outlined in Tom's worry book. Use a *red pencil* to show Luke's level of power and *green pencil* to show Tom's level of power on this rating.

1	2	3	4	5	6	7	8	9	10

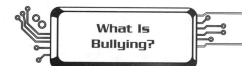

MORE ABOUT IT

Read, discuss, consider, *and* answer *the question about each of these scenarios.*

Scenario	Is it bullying? Explain.
1. Luca thinks the new boy at school is a loser, so he keeps saying he will eat lunch with him and then disappears to play with his friends, leaving the new boy sitting alone.	
2. A group of girls always spend their free time practicing their acrobatic moves. One of the girls has difficulty with her elbow stands, so the other girls try to help her, but she gets upset, cries, and runs away.	
3. Xin Yi has recently moved here from China. She is having trouble with English. A few girls are trying to help her, but there is a group of girls who use strange accents to imitate everything she says and then laugh.	
4. Robert and his friend are joining the school glee club. They are worried that some of the kids at school will make fun of them, so they decide to keep it a secret. Tricia finds out and decides it shouldn't be a secret, because Robert and his friend are fantastic singers. So she decides to tell everyone in their grade.	
5. The class has just completed a midyear spelling test. The students have to trade papers for marking. Olivia knows she has done terribly and doesn't want to swap her work—but does. Ben is responsible for marking Olivia's work. While he marks her work, he writes the crosses really big and shows his friends. Ben and his friends think it's really funny.	
6. Sofia's mother always packs a traditional Greek lunch for her; it's really yummy but nothing like the other kids' lunches. No one will sit next to her because they say that her lunch looks and smells too funny!	

Focus

To read and discuss a narrative in which someone is subject to different forms of bullying and to understand that even "mild" bullying can cause great distress

Teacher Information

- Bullying can broadly be categorized as *physical, social,* or *psychological*. Depending on the circumstances, bullying acts can feature in any category.

  Physical bullying involves direct contact between the bully and the target. It can include causing physical injury and damaging or stealing property.

  Social bullying includes any action on the part of the bully that makes the target feel humiliated or embarrassed in front of his or her peers or excluded by them.

  Psychological bullying includes following or stalking, silently threatening intent to harm, gestures, and subtle exclusion. (Refer to pages *v–vi* for further information.)

Introduction

- The activity is designed to promote discussion about different forms of bullying and to highlight the devastating effect that even seemingly innocuous behavior can have on a target while the perpetrators see it simply as highly amusing.

- For the activity on page 13, discuss strategies that Sofia could adopt to end or minimize each form of bullying. What consequences might these strategies have, and how might Sofia's life change as a result of implementing them?

Discussing the Text

- Explain briefly what the three main forms of bullying are. Give examples. What bullying behaviors is Sofia being subjected to? Which are physical, social, and psychological forms of bullying?

- Why is Sofia is being bullied? (Because of her academic achievement)

- How do we know that Sofia is being bullied and not just subject to occasional unpleasant teasing? (She says, "lots of times each day" and she uses the words *always, whenever, every time*.)

- Bullying is the delivery of deliberate, repeated behaviors with the intent to cause harm. Is bullying more severe if the acts are more serious?

- Why might Sofia's friends have deserted her? (They are afraid of the same treatment; they do not want to be associated with her because she is being so humiliated.)

- Why has she not reported the bullying? (She thinks the behaviors are too insignificant.)

Answers

Page 12

1. Physical: trash being put in her bag, books being hidden, jacket thrown on the floor

   Social: notes being passed around, deliberate exclusion, name-calling

   Psychological: whispering and laughing at her, knowing gestures between peers, making silly noises

2. They are indirect. The perpetrator is not obvious. They do not cause personal injury. They could easily be construed as accidents.

3. Psychological bullying is very difficult to prove, so the bully may continue without fear of being caught and the target is less likely to report it. It is a very effective way to maintain power over a target.

4. What the bully actually does is irrelevant. No one has the right to bully another. All bullying is damaging. The emotional cost to a target cannot be measured by how serious the act is, since the resilience of targets varies.

Page 13

Teacher check

Supporting activity

- Create a "bullying basket" into which students "throw" their bullying behavior. Discuss types of bullying behavior prevalent in the class/school. Assign a wastebasket as the bullying basket. Using dark marker pens, students write individual acts of bullying behavior on sheets of paper. The bullying behaviors are not meant to be exclusive to any student; the whole class is taking joint responsibility for stamping out the problem regardless of the main culprits.

  Sitting in a circle with the wastebasket in the center, students take turns reading out their bullying behavior before lightly scrunching it into a ball and throwing it in the bullying basket. Throwing bullying behavior in the basket makes the statement, "This type of behavior is not acceptable."

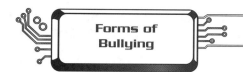
READ ABOUT IT

"I've baked your favorite cake!" called Mom as she heard Sofia drop her schoolbags in the hall. What she heard next came as a surprise. Sofia's bedroom door slammed shut. Startled, but needing to stay calm, Mom knocked gently on the door. "What's up, sweetheart? Can I come in?"

Seeing her 11-year-old daughter sobbing uncontrollably, face-down on the bed, brought tears to Mom's eyes. What could have happened to her happy, friendly, precious child? She sat down beside Sofia and gently stroked her hair, saying nothing but letting her daughter know that she was there for her and ready to listen.

Eventually, Sofia sat up. As Mom held her close, Sofia began to speak and the cause of her distress soon became clear. Sofia was being bullied.

"It's not big things, Mom, nothing I could report to Mrs. Da Silva, but it's happening lots of times every single day and it's just wearing me down. I can't take it anymore."

Mom held Sofia close and let her continue.

"It started with just a few things that I thought were accidents, like a banana skin in my bag, books going missing and then turning up somewhere unusual, and my jacket always on the floor when I was sure I'd hung it up. Then today, a couple of girls exploded into laughter as I picked someone's apple core out of my bag and threw it in the trash. They ran off, and I saw them talking to a group of friends and then they all laughed. They were all looking at me, so I know it was me they were laughing at."

"Do you suspect anyone in particular?" Mom asked softly, not wanting to give away her own feelings of anger.

"It's just too hard to say, Mom. They raise their eyes and giggle when I walk into class, even ones I thought were my friends! Then they pass notes around. I always see them and hear them whisper, loudly so I can hear, 'Not to Sofia!' I don't know what's written on them. It might be nothing. I think they just want me to feel left out.

"I've even stopped answering questions in class now. Every time I say something, someone makes a silly noise and Mrs. Da Silva forgets me and tries to find out who's being silly. Whenever I get praised, they roll their eyes and whisper 'teacher's pet.' I just can't be bothered working hard to keep up my good grades anymore."

"Who do you spend time with at recess and at lunch?" asked Mom, dreading the answer she knew she was going to get.

"No one wants to spend time with me. It's so awful, eating alone and wandering around at recess wishing I was invisible. I really am 'Sofia-no-friends.' I don't know what's happened to my friends. Some of them look at me guiltily, like they're about to say they're sorry, but then they just run off.

"Why me, Mom? What have I done wrong? I used to be so happy at school, but now I feel so alone. Please don't make me go back there, Mom. Please don't—not ever."

As Mom cradled Sofia in her arms, the heartbroken young girl held on tightly and her hot tears began to flow again.

WRITE ABOUT IT

Record your answers after discussing the text on page 11.

1. Give examples of each form of bullying.

	From the text	**Others that you know**
Physical		
Social		
Psychological (mental)		

2. How is the physical bullying that Sofia is experiencing different from something like kicking or punching?

3. Why do you think some bullies use psychological bullying to taunt their targets?

All forms of bullying include acts that range from the childish to the very serious.

For example, physical bullying may move from repeatedly knocking someone's bag on the floor to causing serious injury to someone.

4. Do you think bullying is a problem only if serious acts are used? Give reasons for your answer.

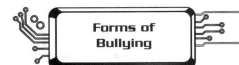

MORE ABOUT IT

1. What strategies would you suggest to help Sofia overcome each form of bullying? Describe what you think the consequences of each would be.

Bullying	Strategies	Consequences
Physical		
Social		
Psychological (mental)		

2. Write a diary entry that Sofia might have written one month after listening to your advice. Focus on each form of bullying and how it has changed.

Dear Diary ...

Focus

To read and discuss a play script in which various aspects of the physical form of bullying are identified and described

Teacher Information

- Bullying can broadly be categorized as *physical, social,* or *psychological*. Depending on the circumstances, bullying acts can feature in any category. (Refer to pages *v–vi* for further information.)

  Physical bullying involves direct contact between the bully and the target. It can include causing physical injury and damaging or stealing property.

  Social bullying includes any actions on the part of the bully that make the target feel humiliated or embarrassed in front of her peers or excluded by them.

  Psychological bullying includes following or stalking, silently threatening intent to harm, gestures, and subtle exclusion. (Refer to pages *v–vi* for further information.)

Introduction

- The play script describes examples of bullying behavior towards a timid student who has been targeted for bullying because of the body language he displays. The behaviors include name calling and threats, intimidation that threatens physical abuse, extortion in which food is demanded to avoid physical injury, damage to the target's property, and theft of the target's possessions.

- In designing icons for each form of bullying for the activity on page 17, students will be thinking more of what each form involves. This will reinforce their understanding of each and, hopefully, make them think twice before using that behavior in the future.

Discussing the Text

- What does the title, *Fear in the Schoolyard*, refer to? (Bullying)

  What does Katelyn mean when she says, "… only worse because it's real life …"? (Bullying is a horrible experience that, unlike a movie, is happening to the target in real life.)

- What specific acts of bullying are addressed in the students' play? (Name-calling, threats, intimidation, extortion, theft, and damage to property) Which acts are physical? Which are social? Which are psychological forms of bullying?

- How much information do you think Antek will give the teacher?

Answers

Page 16

1. (a) false   (b) true   (c) false

2. social

3. It was an act of physical bullying (damage to property) used to reinforce a threat.

4.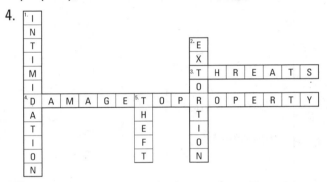

Page 17

Teacher check

Supporting Activity

- Divide the class into groups and give each a physical bullying scenario to script and perform for the rest of the class. For each scenario, create two outcomes, one where the target is repeatedly dominated by the bully and one where he or she overcomes the bully. Discuss the attacks, outcomes, and consequences of each scenario.

READ ABOUT IT

A group of students is planning an assembly item about bullying.

Jordan: We could do a short play about different forms of bullying at school.

Antek: It sounds like a horror movie! Let's call it *Fear in the Schoolyard!*

Katelyn: Well, for some kids it is like that, only worse because it's real life. It happens much more than we realize, in all sorts of ways.

Jordan: Like what, for instance … punching and name-calling?

Jordan pretends to punch Antek in the ribs and calls him "Loser."

Katelyn: Yes, but bullying's much more than just that. It's about having power over someone and how it affects you, socially and mentally.

Tasha: My friend was bullied just because she was shy. She was always being made fun of and left out of things. She should have let someone know before it got so bad.

Antek: You can be bullied online, too. Cyberbullying happens a lot now.

Students exit stage left and enter a few moments later, stage right.

Antek: *(to audience) Fear in the Schoolyard!* by Antek, Jordan, Katelyn, and Tasha.

Tasha and Jordan stand together on one side. Antek approaches them slowly.
Katelyn remains in the wings.

Tasha: *(nods towards Antek)* This one's fair game. Look how his shoulders are all hunched and he's looking down like he's searching the ground for loose change.

Jordan: *(swaggers confidently over to Antek)* Hey, Squirt! What's in your bag?

Antek: *(mumbles)* Nothing.

Tasha: *(annoyed)* Now we all know that's a lie, Squirt … and people who tell lies get punished. Let's see what we've got here. *(Snatches the bag and looks inside)* Mmm, what a great pencil case. I'll take that.

Jordan: *(menacingly)* Now then, Squirt, we're much bigger than you. Meet us here at the same time every day and make sure you've got something nice to give us.

Tasha: *(holds out one of Antek's books)* And Squirt, just in case you were thinking of squealing … don't! *(Rips the book)* Get it?

Katelyn enters stage right.

Katelyn: *(strides confidently towards them)* Tasha! Return Antek's things immediately, and both of you, apologize!

Jordan and Tasha: *(sheepishly)* Sorry, Antek.

Katelyn: Both of you go to my office immediately. I'll be there shortly. Now, Antek, you tell me exactly what happened …

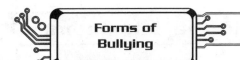
WRITE ABOUT IT

Discuss each question and the text on page 15 before recording your answers.

1. Answer true or false.

    (a) Bullying is just punching and name-calling. _____

    (b) Bullying affects a person physically, socially, and mentally. _____

    (c) Cyberbullying is mostly used to hurt someone physically. _____

2. Circle the correct answer.

    Making fun of people and deliberately excluding them are examples of

    physical   **social**   **psychological** bullying.

3. Why did Tasha rip Antek's book?

_____

4. The excerpts below from the text are clues to the different types of physical bullying found in the text. Write the types of physical bullying in the puzzle.

Across

3. "… people who tell lies get punished" *and*
   "… just in case you were thinking of squealing … don't!"

4. "… don't! *(rips the book)* Get it?"

Down

1. "… (*menacingly*) Now then, Squirt, we're much bigger than you."

2. "… and make sure you've got something nice to give us."

5. "… what a great pencil case. I'll take that."

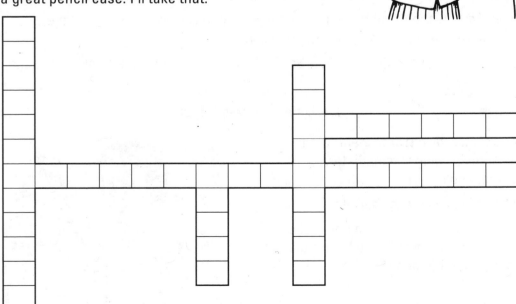

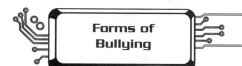

MORE ABOUT IT

There are a number of ways a bully can inflict harm on a target.

No one should have to experience the misery of bullying in any of its forms.

1. Design an icon (a picture) for each form of bullying.

threatening	physical injury	spreading rumors
extortion	cyberbullying	exclusion
damage to property	sneering gestures	loss of property

2. Use your icons to create a poster showing that bullying in any of its forms is unacceptable.

Focus

To read and discuss a journal entry that describes the feelings of the writer, who is the target of psychological bullying

Teacher Information

- Bullying can broadly be categorized as physical, social, or psychological. Depending on the circumstances, bullying acts can feature in any category.

  Physical bullying involves direct contact between the bully and the target. It can include causing physical injury and damaging or stealing property.

  Social bullying includes any actions on the part of the bully that make the target feel humiliated or embarrassed in front of his or her peers or excluded by them.

  Psychological bullying includes following or stalking, silently threatening intent to harm, gestures, and subtle exclusion. (Refer to pages *v–vi* for further information.)

Introduction

- The text does not say if the writer and bullies are boys or girls. The questions assume they are all boys, but they could be either.

- The activity is designed to promote discussion about psychological bullying. Evidence against a psychological bully is difficult to find. He or she neither does nor says anything that can be construed as "unacceptable behavior." Negative body language is used to threaten, intimidate, insult, and exclude. It is all in the way the target interprets the look, the stance, the action. Psychological bullies make the effort to be pleasant to those who are not targets so that accusations leveled by the targets are disbelieved. Knowing this lowers the target's self-esteem even further.

- Ensure that students understand the meaning of "negative body language." This includes facial expressions and eye contact. Demonstrate different forms of body language and classify them as positive or negative.

Discussing the Text

- What are the bullies doing to the writer?

- How are they doing it?

- If they are not physically hurting him, saying mean things, or spreading rumors, why is the writer so upset?

- How badly does the text suggest the target is affected by the bullying?

- How do you think the writer could help himself out of this situation?

Answers

Page 20

1. Psychological bullying is a way to offend targets and seriously damage their self-esteem, since they believe that everyone, in addition to the bullies, thinks or feels bad things about them. It makes the targets feel very self-conscious.

2. intimidated: "silently, menacingly, they follow me home."

   threatened: "Their glares shout, 'Danger—watch out!'"

   insulted: "I slink to my desk, my body pierced by the lethal lasers of their glowering stares."

   excluded: "Looking at me with smirks and sneers, Their eyes agree, 'Not him—leave him 'til last.'"

3. The psychological bully leaves no evidence and is pleasant to everyone else. It would be hard to believe he or she has done anything wrong.

4. They always walk behind him, stopping if he stops. They are silent. They stand, staring at his house for a while before walking away.

5. (a) They use their eyes to speak to the writer and to each other about the writer.

   (b) It is difficult for anyone else to detect it.

6. They are so friendly with the bullies that they don't even see him or recognize his misery.

Page 21

Teacher check

Supporting Activity

- Reporting psychological bullying is too difficult for many targets because it is so hard to prove. Brainstorm a list of negative body language that you could look out for in a person accused of bullying. Play Charades, identifying the example of bullying that each form of body language shows.

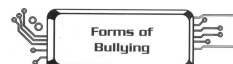
READ ABOUT IT

Psychological bullying plays with the mind. It includes ignoring, excluding, and using negative body gestures, all designed to lower the target's self-esteem.

- *Targets are often reluctant to report psychological bullying because it is difficult to prove.*
- *Bullies can easily explain their actions or even deny them because they are not obvious to anyone who is not involved.*
- *As a result, many targets of this form of bullying suffer in silence.*

I can feel them behind me. I know they are there.
When I stop and turn, they stop too,
Standing, watching. What can I do?
Silently, menacingly, they follow me home.
Outside the house, they stand and stare before moving on.

In class, the teacher thinks that I don't understand the lessons.
I raise my hand to let her know that I do have the answers.
But their eyes meet mine, daring me to speak.
Their glares shout, "Danger—watch out!"
They alone can be at the top of the class.

What can I do? How can I stop them?
They're doing nothing wrong—or so they would say.
No fights, no arguments, no obvious acts,
But always around, tormenting me silently
Like a dark, warning shadow.

As I walk into the classroom, the buzz of conversation slows.
I slink to my desk, my body pierced by the lethal lasers of their glowering stares.
Head bowed, I lower myself into the chair
To curl up and disappear would be the answer,
Anything to stop this endless scorn.

In sports, they are the best at everything, the perfect leaders.
They pick out their groups from the rest of the class.
Looking at me with smirks and sneers,
Their eyes agree, "Not him—leave him 'til last."
Each name called before mine is a wound in my chest.

Five of them, just one-sixth of the class,
Their command seems all powerful.
But the others seem fine, not bothered at all.
Together, they talk and they laugh, like one happy class.
It's only me who doesn't fit in, like an unwanted visitor.

Is it really happening, or is it just in my head?
It's all I can think about. I just can't take any more!
To the five, I'm their plaything. They enjoy making me feel bad.
To the rest, I'm invisible. I don't exist. I don't count.
Is it really happening, or is it just in my head?

WRITE ABOUT IT

Record your answers after discussing the text on page 19.

1. What is psychological bullying, and how does it make targets feel?

2. Write the lines from the text that describe how the writer is being bullied.

intimidated	
threatened	
insulted	
excluded	

3. Why would psychological bullying be difficult to report to a teacher or a friend?

4. Why does the writer think that the boys are following him?

5. (a) In school, what body language do the bullies use to upset the writer?

   (b) Why is this a "clever" method for the bullies to use?

6. When someone is being psychologically bullied, his or her self-esteem can be so battered that they start to think that everyone is against them, even if they are not.

   How does the writer feel about the rest of the class?

Is It Just in My Head? – 3

MORE ABOUT IT

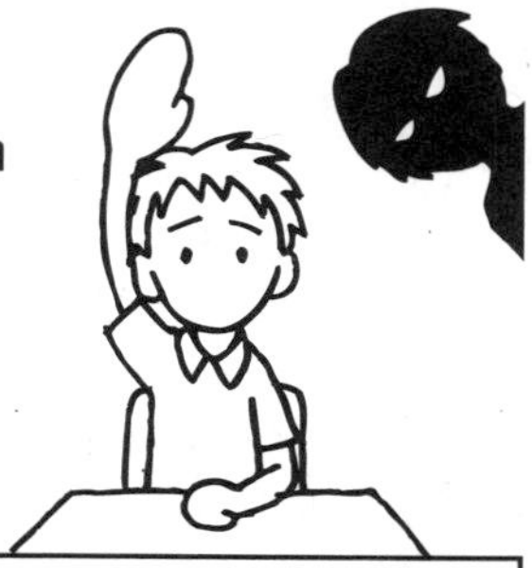

With psychological bullying, bullies use negative body language to communicate with their targets.

- *Illustrate examples of negative body language to show the forms of psychological bullying listed below.*
- *Write a brief explanation of your illustration.*

Ignoring	**Intimidating**
My illustration shows	*My illustration shows*
Insulting	**Threatening**
My illustration shows	*My illustration shows*

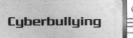

Focus

To read and discuss a newspaper article that clearly defines "cyberbullying"

Teacher Information

- Cyberbullying is the act of bullying a target using technology such as cell phones or the Internet as vehicles.

- In the "real world" there are generally physical boundaries where the bullying stops—for example, at home or in the classroom (with the teacher present). However, cyberspace knows no boundaries, and a target has no reprieve or safe haven from his or her tormentor.

- Cyberbullying includes repeated attacks, threats, defamation, or harassment designed to cause distress to the intended target. The bully or group of bullies may use cell phone messages or pictures, Internet social sites or blogs, or e-mail to render their torment. They may stage the same attack over and over or vary the delivery. It may be organized by one bully and carried out by several others, or it may be organized and carried out by the same person.

- Cyberspace provides bullies with a sense of anonymity that they don't have in the "real world." It allows them to take the bullying to a level beyond what is possible at school or other "traditional bullying hot spots." It also provides the target with a hard copy of the event(s), which are then able to be read and reread many times over—causing much deeper harm.

Introduction

- The newspaper article discusses cyberbullying as if it were a type of disease. However, most diseases can be cured, or at least the symptoms can be diminished. Cyberbullying is growing at a rate much faster than anything ever seen before, and governments and police are struggling to keep up. Outdated laws do not provide specific powers to step in and deal with the types of situations that are arising.

Discussing the Text

- Before reading the article, ask students if they have an understanding of "cyberbullying." (Some students may be quite savvy, while others have a fair idea but because of careful monitoring by parents they have not had exposure to it.)

- Why do you think a newspaper felt this article was important enough to write? (Because the incidence of bullying via cell phones and the Internet has increased so dramatically in recent years. It is a newsworthy story designed to inform the public of the issue.)

Supporting Activities

- View the online video:

  <http://www.acmi.net.au/vid_cyber_bullying.htm>

- The online video above shows just one form of cyberbullying. Ask students to create their own videos, in small groups, to show another form of cyberbullying.

Answers

Teacher check

READ ABOUT IT

NEW DISEASE SPREADS FAST!

BROCK ROBERTS

A new disease is spreading across our planet faster than any before. The disease spreads like a cancer and multiplies at a great rate of knots— CYBERBULLYING.

Technology, such as cell phones and the Internet, which was developed to make lives easier, is actually making life very uncomfortable for a growing number of people. Breaching the safety of homes, cyberbullying knows no boundaries. Any time of the day or night, cyberbullies can strike, attacking their targets anytime and anywhere!

Some bullies attack their targets for weeks, months, and even years. Where some cyberbullies work alone, other employ groups to administer their wrath.

Psychologists are battling to find a solution before the war is lost altogether.

"Calling it a war is certainly not overstating the problem—and it's a war we can't afford to lose!" states the respected head of psychology at Edinhouse University.

It is impossible to estimate the extent of cyberbullying within the community because not all instances are reported. Police recommend keeping all text messages and printing out all e-mail or social networking communications in order to report a cyberbullying situation in detail.

WRITE ABOUT IT

Discuss and record your thoughts about each of these.

(a) Brock Roberts compared cyberbullying to a disease such as cancer.

(b) Your own home is no longer considered "your one safe place."

(c) Psychologists refer to cyberbullying as a "war"—one we cannot afford to lose.

(d) Only some people report instances of cyberbullying to the police.

MORE ABOUT IT

Consider modern technology. Discuss and record on a separate sheet of paper:

(a) types of technology available

(b) how each is used by you and your peers

(c) the positive and negative impacts of this technology.

Focus

To read and discuss a page from a social networking site created to "attack" another student

Teacher Information

- Traditional bullying can be observed by as few as two or three people or as large a group as ten or more people. However, current technology allows the bullying to be witnessed and carried on by a far greater audience—adding to the target's humiliation.

- This form of bullying can also be continued over a longer period and total strangers can join in—almost like a ripple in a pond, it can grow and grow. Every time someone forwards a text message or e-mail, that person is helping the bully continue his or her campaign against the target. (Refer to page *vi* for further information.)

Introduction

- This page was modeled on a real-life situation; however, the language and innuendo have been watered down considerably (on the original page, the bully wanted the target "dead").

- The page provides a hard copy for students to discuss and observe. They may have seen or be aware of similar pages circulating. It would be a good idea to ascertain if there are any such pages currently circulating.

- In the "More About It" activity, students are given an insight into the other side of the coin, the "target." Students are encouraged to reflect upon the target's behavior as well as the behavior of the bullies and the bystanders.

Discussing the Text

- Ask the students if any of them are familiar with social networking sites. Ascertain how many students use these types of sites, how often, and why they use these sites. (This information can assist you in directing your attention to students who use these types of sites and are at risk of encountering such issues.)

- Ask students to identify why they think Jac has been targeted on this site. (Answers to this will vary, since Jac isn't your typical target. He is quite self-confident. However, the anonymity of the Internet allows the bully additional power that he or she might not normally have in a traditional situation.)

- Ask students what type of person the creator of this page might be. Do you think you would recognize this type of person if you met him or her? (We want students to identify that bullies, in particular cyberbullies, don't walk around with a sign on their head saying "I'm a bully!" A bully can be anybody, even someone you trust as a good friend.)

Answers

Page 26

1. (a) No; Answers will vary; however, people often join the conversation on social networking pages without considering the purpose or impact of the page on others.

    (b) Answers will vary; the name of the bully is "Destroy Jac Jacson," which allows the bully to remain anonymous, giving him or her more power than in real life.

    (c) Answers will vary.

    (d) The page creator obviously thinks of himself or herself as something of a "champion" bully and is quite proud of his or her achievements in the past.

2. (a) No; Answers will vary.

    (b) He could contact the administrators of FACEspace to have the page removed, and he could also contact the police to have them deal with the situation.

    (c) Answers will vary.

Page 27

1. Discussion will vary.

2. (a) No. He should tell everyone the real reason for leaving the school, since this would take away the bully's power or at least the perception of power.

    (b) The bullies have made his life miserable, but Jac has managed to stay strong and remain focused.

    (c) high self-esteem, resilient, focused, etc.

3. Answers will vary.

Supporting Activities

- View the video at:

    <http://www.digizen.org/cyberbullying/australia/fullFilm.aspx>

- View the video *Lauren's Ordeal* at:

    <http://www.cybersmart.gov.au/wiseuptoit/videoclips.htm>

- Discuss both scenarios of cyberbullying. Ask students to select one character and write a journal entry from that character's point of view.

- Ask students to work in small groups to create their own scenario. Perform these in front of the class or for other classes at the school.

READ ABOUT IT

FACEspace Search Home Profile Account ▼

Destroy Jac Jacson LIKE

Wall   Info   Photos   Discussions

Add to my page's favorites

Suggest to friends

Just because we can! Join in and lets make Jac's life a living nightmare!

1,725 people like this

Tyler K   Sam   TJ

Deano   Kristy   Stace

Bobby   Cal

Create a page

Report Page

SHARE

 Destroy Jac Jacson Mission complete! lol
hes gonna be leavin the skool 4 good1 hahahaha
now whos next????????? >. <
March 17 at 4:23 · Comment · Like

 Destroy Jac Jacson im gonna finish him off tomoz!!
lol had enuf of his smartbrain ....watch nd lern guyz!!
hehehe … the master at work
March 8 at 6:17 · Comment · Like

 Deano need any help dude????
March 8 at 6:32 · Comment · Like

 Dotty uncool, you guyz need to get a life: O
March 8 at 6:54 · Comment · Like

 Destroy Jac Jacson watch out dotty, u mite b next hahaha
March 8 at 7:17 · Comment · Like

 Destroy Jac Jacson didya see me trip him afta hockey????? hahahah
this is just the beginning dude; (watch out!)
January 28 at 4:04 · Comment · Like

 Kristy hahahaha serious!!!! that was heaps kool!! thought he
was gonna cry
January 28 at 4:10 · Comment · Like

 Deano wot we doin tomoz?? we could get him in art>.<
January 28 at 4:17 · Comment · Like

 Destroy Jac Jacson feel free to join in on the destruction my
friends hahahahaha
January 28 at 4:32 · Comment · Like

 Destroy Jac Jacson wants him gone hahaha
January 24 at 5:18 · Comment · Like

 Sam yeah me 2 sick of him being so good at everything
January 24 at 6:25 · Comment · Like

 Stace kool can i join in 2 hate how hes such a teachers pet
January 24 at 6:57 · Comment · Like

Older posts ▼

WRITE ABOUT IT

1. Use the information provided on the FACEspace page to answer these.

   (a) Do you think 1,725 people actually know Jac Jacson? **Yes** **No**
   Why do you think so many people like this page?

   _____

   _____

   (b) Did you notice the main perpetrator of the bullying is actually anonymous? **Yes** **No**
   What does this tell you about the bully?

   _____

   _____

   (c) Dotty seems to be the only one prepared to speak against the page creator.
   What might happen to her?

   _____

   _____

   _____

   (d) What do you think the page creator means when he or she says:
   "watch nd lern guyz!! hehehe ...... the master at work"?

   _____

   _____

2. Now think about and discuss each of these. Record your thoughts.

   (a) Of the 1725 people who like this page, there are only a handful of people participating in the actual bullying. The remainder of the people are bystanders.

   Do you think it is okay to "like" a page like this?

   Explain your answer. **Yes** **No**

   (b) If Jac Jacson were aware of this page, what do you think he could do about it?

   (c) What punishment would be fitting for the creator and fans of this "hate" page?

(a)
(b)
(c)

MORE ABOUT IT

1. Read and discuss this entry from Jac's journal.

March 15
So happy! I won the scholarship to Newberry School to pursue
hockey! Can't wait to go to school tomorrow and tell everyone
I'll be leaving at the end of the year. Have to say, I won't
be sorry to see the back of some of the kids at school. They
have made my life miserable over the past few months—dunno
why!
Won't tell them why I'm leavin', let them think they won! But
I'll be having the last laugh!!
Nothin' can get me down!!!!

2. After reading and discussing this entry …

   (a) do you think Jac is doing the right thing by letting his bullies think they have "won"?

   _____

   _____

   (b) what impact do you think the bullies have had on Jac?

   _____

   _____

   (c) can you identify and list some of Jac's character traits?

   _____

   _____

   _____

   _____

3. Consider the future impact …

on Jac.	on the bully.

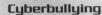
Focus

To read and discuss Cal's blog, used to inform his audience about what to do if they find themselves the target of cyberbullying

Teacher Information

- Fortunately, online communication and information provide a level of security that cannot be found in real life. It is education about and understanding of the technology that will provide a safe and secure environment. Individuals have the ability to lock their profile, blog, or webpage—allowing only selected friends access to the information, while particular callers can be blocked from a person's cell-phone contact list.

- Individuals also need to be aware of the information they share with others. It is up to the individual to carefully consider the sharing of photographs, information, and personal events. By taking simple precautions, individuals can take charge and reduce the risk of becoming an online target.

- The "upside" of cyberbullying is that it provides a hard copy that can be saved and used as evidence against the bully. The target must be educated to save and keep all documentation and share it with the appropriate authorities (school, parent, law enforcement officers) to have the matter dealt with. Criminal legislation is now available to pursue any specific behaviors involving such technology to cause harm to another person.

- Refer to page *vi* for further information.

Introduction

- The key feature of this text is to provide students with a simple, step-by-step approach to deal with a cyberbullying situation.

- A lot of literature on the Internet recommends that anyone being cyberbullied should: STOP — BLOCK — REPORT!

Discussing the Text

- How is cyberbullying different from traditional bullying? (The students need to identify that cyberbullying has no boundaries or limitations, but it also provides the target with hard evidence that can be used to his or her advantage when reporting cyberbullying to the authorities.)

- If cyberbullying happens to you or someone you know, what should you always remember? (The students should acknowledge that it is something that happens to a lot of people and there are ways to deal with the situation if they ask for help.)

- What could you do if you were a witness to an instance of cyberbullying? (Students need to identify that bystander behavior makes them as bad as the bully and that as good citizens they should discreetly help the target without drawing attention to themselves.)

Answers

Pages 30–31

Teacher check

Supporting Activity

- View this webpage outlining how to stop contact on various social sites:

  <http://www.thinkuknow.org. au/site/stop.asp>

- Ask students to create a webpage that educates children their own age about how to deal with cyberbullies.

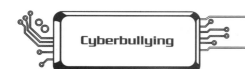
READ ABOUT IT

Cal's blOgSPOT

MONDAY, JULY 19, 2010

Unless you have been buried in space, you would be aware that the world is changing—and not always for the better. The technological revolution—which was designed to help us—has a darker side!

Online harassment is the NEW way to attack a target! I should know, I have been a target! The worst part is that it is relentless—24/7—without a break. What made it 100 times worse than traditional bullying was that everyone could see it, even people I didn't know became involved. I found myself drawn to the site to see what was being written about me and who was writing it. Reading it over and over and over didn't help either! It was the most horrific experience of my life—but I have learned some really valuable lessons, which I want to share.

Firstly, you must always remember that it is NEVER your fault if you have become the target of online harassment. Secondly, follow these easy steps:

NEVER	share your password.
ALWAYS	make your security questions really hard to guess.
THINK	carefully about what has been said online. Do you think the person intentionally set out to be unpleasant or are you being super-sensitive?
TELL	the person if you think a "joke" has gone too far or if you have been hurt by something he or she has said.

If it continues …

NEVER	respond to the bully. This will only inflame the situation and give the bully what he or she wants.
KEEP	the evidence. Copy and paste all text into a word processor document and keep it in a specific folder on your desktop. Remember to include all dates and times.
BLOCK	or delete the bully. If you can't be reached, you can't be hurt.
REPORT	the events to your parents or guardians. Also report the person or page to the social network site admin. If the bullying is really severe or continues excessively, report it to the police!

Always remember, you are not alone—this happens to more than 20% of kids—that's one in five! The most important thing is to TALK to parents, the school, the social site, and the police. It can be dealt with and stopped and, one day, you can go back to your computer without fear!

about cal ▶

please share
 SHARE

join Cal's rss feed

search Cal's blogSPOT

Search

blog archive

2010 (32) ▼
July (3) ▼
   July 19
   July 10
   July 02
  June (6) ▶
  May (9) ▶
  April (4) ▶
  March (5) ▶
  February (3) ▶
  January (2) ▶
2009 (28) ▶
2008 (37) ▶
2007 (23) ▶

contact cal
cal@cybermail.com

Cal's blogSPOT stats
123,455 hits

WRITE ABOUT IT

1. Use the information on the Cyber Protection – 1 page to answer these.

   (a) Rate the value of the information provided by Cal in his blog.

1	2	3	4	5	6	7	8	9	10

   ▼ poor   ▼ exceptional

   Explain your rating.

   _____

   _____

   (b) Cal provides some key strategies to use in a bullying situation. Which one would you consider to be the most important? Why?

   _____

   _____

   _____

   (c) Considering Cal's recommendation to "TALK," list five people that you trust enough to tell about such a situation.

2. Discuss each of these in a small group and record your ideas.

   (a) What does Cal mean when he says: "Unless you have been buried in space, you would be aware that the world is changing—and not always for the better"?

   _____

   _____

   (b) Cal states: "The technological revolution—which was designed to help us—has a darker side!" Is it that technology has a dark side, or is it that some people choose to use technology in a negative way? Think about this and write your thoughts.

   _____

   _____

   _____

   (c) Cal also states that "online harassment" is worse than "traditional bullying." Identify his reasons and add some of your own.

   _____

   _____

   _____

MORE ABOUT IT

1. Insert your name into the screen below.

2. Explain how being the target of this type of cyber-bullying would make you feel.

3. Outline three steps you would take to deal with this type of situation.

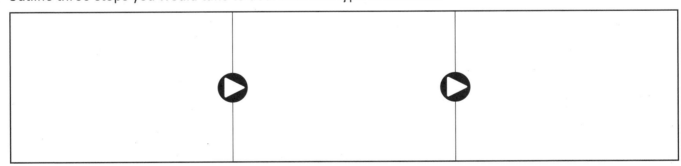

4. Explain why you would deal with the situation in the way you have chosen.

5. Discuss and comment:

"It's bad enough that there were witnesses to this humiliating event; however, the embarrassment is made worse by the fact that it was recorded and is now being passed on indiscriminately to hundreds, possibly thousands of people."

What impact do you think this has on the target?

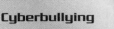

Focus

To read about and discuss how various cyberbullying scenarios can lead to serious charges being brought against the perpetrator(s)

Teacher Information

- The first thing that needs to be made clear is that there are no laws against cyberbullying, just as there are no laws against bullying. The way criminal justice deals with it is by charging perpetrators with explicit charges of stalking, assault and battery, harassment, or threats against life or property.

- Secondly, police do take instances of cyberbullying seriously, provided evidence of the episodes can be provided. They are able to use technology to trace calls, and IP addresses can lead them to the perpetrator(s).

- Refer to page *vi* for further information.

Introduction

- The three scenarios depicted in this activity are common in terms of cyberbullying. It is important to show students that there are consequences for such actions or for being involved in such behavior.

- Penalties for each type of offense can vary from state to state.

Discussing the Text

- Why do you think the penalties are so severe? (Students should identify that the offenses themselves are severe and that they have a great negative impact upon the victim.)

- What other types of behavior do you think should be penalized? Why, and what type of penalities should be applied? (Encourage students to think about various types of behavior that are often utilized in cases of cyberbullying, and to consider the effect on the target and the seriousness of the behavior.)

Answers

Teacher check

Supporting Activity

- Invite students to create an anti-cyberbullying campaign that educates people about the consequences of initiating or participating in cyberbullying. The aim of the campaign is to reduce the incidence of cyberbullying in the community.

READ ABOUT IT

A social networking site is set up to attack another student in the school based on his race. It is an open forum, so everyone is welcome to participate.

**RACIAL VILIFICATION
3 YEARS' IMPRISONMENT**

A group of girls regularly sends menacing text messages and e-mails to a classmate over a long period of time.

**HARASSMENT
3 YEARS' IMPRISONMENT**

Explicit text messages and e-mails are used to send threats to harm or kill another classmate.

**THREATS TO KILL OR HARM
7 YEARS' IMPRISONMENT**

WRITE ABOUT IT

Discuss and record your thoughts about each of these.

(a) If this type of bullying was happening to a friend of yours, what advice would you give?

_____

_____

_____

(b) After reading these examples of penalties, do you think it is worthwhile to keep the evidence and report any incidence of cyberbullying to the police?   `Yes` `No`

Explain. _____

_____

(c) Knowing that there are penalties involved in this type of behavior, do you now think that you would be less likely to participate?   `Yes` `No`

Explain. _____

_____

MORE ABOUT IT

Discuss and research the following.

In addition to the offenses shown above, there are also offenses such as:

- *stalking*
- *assault*
- *fraud (or impersonation).*

(a) Find out what type of behavior constitutes each of these offenses.

(b) Find out the penalties for each of these offenses.

Focus

To read and discuss a selection of scenarios to identify targets of bullying

Teacher Information

- While anyone can be bullied, bullies generally target an individual or group because they are different in some way and part of a minority. This makes them an easier target than if they were part of a mainstream group. Bullies tend to find children easier to target if they are vulnerable—shy, insecure, find it hard to stand up for themselves, and get upset (cry) easily. Bullies get a bigger reaction from these victims, which gives the bullies the sense of power they are after. Forms of bullying used against these victims are usually of the direct type—for example, verbal or physical abuse or negative body language—the bully gets an immediate reaction. However, self-assured children can also be targets. Indirect forms of bullying are more likely to be used—for instance, isolation, taking possessions, or cyberbullying.

- Examples of minority groups targeted by bullies include those from a different race, religious faith, or culture; those who have a different (or perceived) sexual orientation, physical ability, or physical feature(s); those who have a high or low intellectual ability or social status; and those who have a vulnerable, sensitive personality. (Refer to page *vii* for further information.)

Introduction

- Each of the nine scenarios on page 35 shows an example of a different minority group that bullies target. Ensure that students understand some of the terms that are likely to be used in discussion:

  target – used to describe the victim being bullied

  discriminate – to treat unfairly because someone is different in some way

  minority group – a category of people smaller in number than the majority, who are discriminated against for some reason

  vulnerable (personality) – someone who is highly sensitive and likely to be hurt emotionally

Discussing the Text

Refer to answers for required responses.

- Why do you think bullies usually target an individual or group that is in the minority?
- How was each person bullied?
- What minority group was each person from?
- For what reason was each target bullied?

Answers

Page 36

1.

Difference in ...	Scenario	Target(s)/Reason
(a) race	3	Aneeta & Anya/skin color, accent, hairstyle
(b) religion	4	Rahmad/difference in celebrating religious festival
(c) culture	6	Raoul/different food and the way it was prepared
(d) sexual orientation	2	Lachlan/believed to be "gay" because of love of dance
(e) physical ability	7	Isobel/lack of netball skills
(f) intellectual ability	8	Lia/academic achievements
(g) physical features	9	Callum/protruding ears
(h) social status	5	Abbey/appearance and state of possessions due to lower economic class
(i) personality traits	1	Josh/sensitive, vulnerable nature

2. Answers should indicate that self-assured characters are more likely to stand up to a bully and aren't as likely to be a target.

3. Answers may vary. Sympathetic teacher guidance is needed for discussion on this topic.

4. Answers should indicate that bullies target minority groups because their differences makes them an easier target than a larger, mainstream group.

Page 37

Teacher check

Supporting Activity

- The students choose one of the scenarios and write a conversation between themselves and the target(s) that gives details about one of the times the target was bullied.

READ ABOUT IT

Scenario 1

Josh is shy, lacks confidence, and finds it hard to maintain friendships. He hates going to school because he is bullied constantly. A group of three boys do things such as put his lunch in the trash or put sand in it, kick him sneakily during football games, and corner him if he takes the shortcut home down the alley.

Scenario 2

Lachlan is an accomplished dancer, having had lessons from an early age in classical ballet, jazz ballet, and tap. Students in his class call him "gay" and a "girl" and make exaggerated dance step movements and arm gestures. Someone has also changed his profile picture on a social networking site to a ballerina.

Scenario 3

Aneeta and Anya are twin sisters who are new to the school, having come from an African nation. In the few weeks they've been at the school, no one has asked them to join in activities during break times. Some are making fun of the girls' dark skin, tight black braids, and accent.

Scenario 4

During a discussion about religious festivals, Rahmad explained how his family of Middle Eastern origin celebrates one. Since then, two boys have elbowed and punched him in the corridor and tripped him whenever they get the chance. He also believes they started a text rumor that his family belongs to a weird sect.

Scenario 5

Abbey comes from a family that struggles to make ends meet. While her appearance is tidy, her uniform is faded and too small and her lunch box and backpack are showing signs of wear. A group of well-to-do popular girls are always whispering and pointing at her and making sneering remarks when she passes by.

Scenario 6

Raoul asked Harry over to his house one afternoon. The next day, Harry told people at school that Raoul's house stinks of weird smells and his mom makes strange-looking food. Since then, several students pretend to hold their breath when he passes by and call him "Foul Raoul."

Scenario 7

Although Isobel tries hard at basketball practice, she often drops the ball and throws wayward passes. Someone has been hiding her gym bag and emptying her water bottle. Isobel overheard two girls telling others on the squad to throw difficult passes to her during training and not to pass the ball to her during games.

Scenario 8

Lia is an academically talented student who scores the highest marks in tests and always answers the teacher's questions. She has begun receiving upsetting text messages from an unknown number stating that everybody hates her, she's a boring "know-it-all," she'll be excluded from things, and her belongings will disappear.

Scenario 9

Callum has large ears. Even when he tries to comb his hair over them, they eventually protrude. Nearly every day, a couple of students in his class cup their hands behind their ears to make their ears stick out and tauntingly tell him he looks like a "wingnut." They often take Callum's hat off when he's outside and throw it away.

WRITE ABOUT IT

Record your answers after discussing the text on page 35.

Anybody can be bullied, sometimes for a reason and sometimes for no apparent reason. Bullies generally target an individual or group because they are different in some way or vulnerable. The targets are usually part of a minority group.

1. In each of the scenarios on page 35, a bully (or bullies) has targeted someone because he or she is different or vulnerable. Write the number of the scenario next to each difference, the names of the person or persons being bullied [target(s)], and keywords to summarize the reason the target(s) was/were bullied.

Difference in ...	Scenario	Target(s)/Reason
(a) race		
(b) religion		
(c) culture		
(d) sexual orientation		
(e) physical ability		
(f) intellectual ability		
(g) physical features		
(h) social status		
(i) personality traits		

2. Do you think Josh would more likely be a target for bullies if he appeared confident and stood up for himself? Why/Why not?

_____

_____

3. Why do you think some students in Lachlan's class call him "gay" because he dances? _____

_____

_____

4. Why do bullies usually target those from minority groups?

_____

_____

MORE ABOUT IT

Have you been a target for a bully because of being different in some way or being vulnerable? Have you heard about or witnessed someone else being a target for being in a minority group?

Give a brief summary under each heading. Make up an appropriate example, if necessary.

Personality traits	Sexual orientation	Race
Religion	**Social status**	**Culture**
Physical ability	**Intellectual ability**	**Physical features**

Focus

To view and discuss illustrations showing bullying events to identify why people can be targets

Teacher Information

- While anyone can be bullied, bullies generally target an individual or group because they are different in some way and part of a minority. This makes them an easier target than if they were part of a mainstream group. Bullies tend to find children easier to target if they are vulnerable—shy, insecure, find it hard to stand up for themselves, and get upset (cry) easily. Bullies get a bigger reaction from these victims, which gives the bullies the sense of power they are after.

- Examples of minority groups targeted by bullies include those from a different race, religious faith, or culture; those who have a different (or perceived) sexual orientation, physical ability, or physical feature(s); those who have a high or low intellectual ability or social status; and those who have a vulnerable, sensitive personality. (Refer to page *vii* for further information.)

Introduction

- Pages 39–41 would best be completed after pages 35–37 because students will have more background knowledge about the minority groups bullies target. The three illustrations on page 39 show different targets who are being bullied. The students should carefully view the three illustrations, considering why each person might have been made a target.

Discussing the Text

- *Illustration 1:* What text message was sent to the boy with the cell phone? Why might he have been a target for a cyberbully? Does the boy's appearance give any clues? What minority group might he belong to?

- *Illustration 2:* What are the two students in the background doing? What are their expressions? What are the expressions and body language of the students who are being taunted? Does their appearance give an indication as to why they are targets? What minority group might they belong to?

- *Illustration 3:* What is the girl viewing on screen? Why would she be chosen by a cyberbully to be part of a poll? What minority group might she belong to?

Answers

Page 40

1. (a) "every 1 h8s u bc ur a loser!!!!" (Everyone hates you because you are a loser!!!!)

   (b) No, because it has "unknown" in sender box.

   (c) Possible answers: He wears glasses/looks small for his age and is being bullied for having a different physical appearance; he could have a sensitive personality, which bullies target.

2. (a) They are pointing at the students in front of them and laughing and making obviously hurtful remarks.

   (b) They have dark skin and physical features that appear African. The boys look very unhappy and uncomfortable about being taunted by the other students.

   (c) Possible answers: They are from a minority group—a different race, culture, or religion from the students who are bullying.

3. (a) She has found that someone has set up an online poll for others to vote for the ugliest girl in the school and that she is one of the girls in the poll.

   (b) She has 20 votes out of 40, so 50% of the voters consider her the ugliest girl at school.

   (c) Possible answers: She is being targeted because of her physical appearance—she isn't very attractive because of her freckles and hair style.

Page 41

Teacher check

Supporting Activity

- Draw a picture that illustrates a bullying scene that gives clues as to why someone could be a target.

READ ABOUT IT

ILLUSTRATION 1

ILLUSTRATION 2

ILLUSTRATION 3

WRITE ABOUT IT

Record your answers after discussing the illustrations on page 39.

1. (a) What text message has the boy in Illustration 1 read on his cell phone?

_____

_____

(b) Can he tell who sent it?

_____

(c) Write some possible reasons why a bully might have targeted him.

_____

_____

_____

2. (a) Describe what the students in the background in Illustration 2 are doing.

_____

_____

(b) Describe the appearance and expressions of the students in the foreground.

_____

_____

(c) Write some possible reasons why the bullies might have targeted them.

_____

_____

_____

3. (a) What has the girl in Illustration 3 discovered on a website?

_____

_____

(b) How did the girl poll?

_____

_____

(c) Why might she have been chosen as one of the girls in the poll?

_____

_____

MORE ABOUT IT

1. The illustration below shows the boy on page 39 receiving a text bullying message. Imagine what he might be thinking as he reads it. Write his thoughts in the speech bubble.

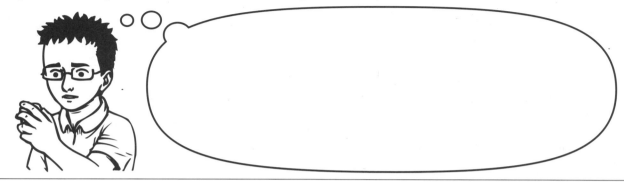

2. The illustration below shows the bullies on page 39. What might the bullies be saying? Write a text in each bully's speech bubble.

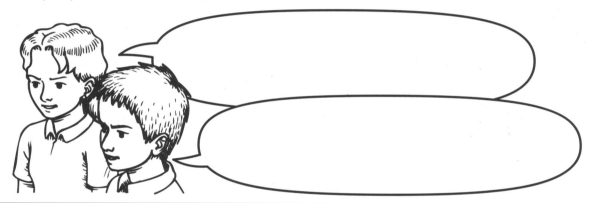

3. The illustration below is one of a computer screen. The girl on page 39 received an online poll voting on her appearance. What is another type of poll a bully might set up and find targets for? Design one and outline it on the screen. Use imaginary names.

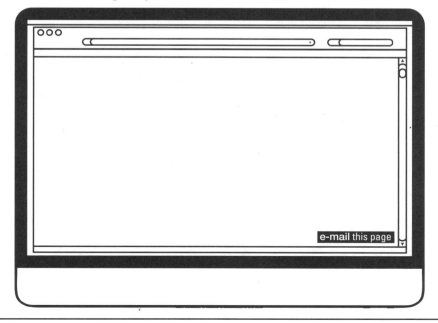

Focus

To read about and discuss the short-term effects of bullying

Teacher Information

- All targets are affected to some degree by bullying. The extent to which they are affected depends greatly on their confidence, self-esteem, and resilience. Some children will have strategies for coping with the bullying, thus ending the problem, but others will suffer consequences in the short and long term.

- For the target, short-term effects can include loss of appetite; insomnia; feelings of sadness, fear, anger, shame, loneliness; excessive absenteeism from school; drop in schoolwork standards; poor attention span; loss of interest in social activities; anxiety attacks; feeling responsible for the attacks; and a lack of trust in friends.

- For the bully, there can also be negative short-term effects, such as shallow friendships (peers are "friends" only because they fear being bullied themselves), negative reputation among school personnel and some students, effects of being unable to deal with his or her emotions and problems appropriately.

Introduction

- The fictitious blog outlines many of the possible short-term effects of bullying on the target. Ensure that students understand the following terms:

  blog   depressed   suicide   stress

  emotional well-being

- Ask the students leading questions before reading the text, such as "How do you feel when you are really stressed or worried about something? How could the emotions caused by being bullied affect different aspects of your life?"

Discussing the Text

- How are the feelings that Jeb has been having affecting aspects of his life? What could be a consequence of Jeb's inability to concentrate at school, and come to school, over a few months? What else could happen if the bullying continues?

Answers

Page 44

1. (a) Jeb's lack of sleep, his stress, and fear mean he is less able to concentrate and learn at school.

   (b) Jeb's fear and worry are affecting his ability to sleep well.

   (c) Jeb does not want to go to school because of the bullying, so his attendance is dropping.

   (d) Depression, fear, worry, and feeling tired will all impact negatively on Jeb's mental and emotional well-being.

   (e) The bullying is leading to a lack of exercise, disturbed sleep, feeling sick, and irregular eating habits, which all impact negatively on Jeb's physical health.

   (f) Jeb's daily routine has changed; he no longer goes for a run, tries to avoid going to school, doesn't eat properly, and is experiencing sleep disruptions.

2. Dean's bullying is affecting his own ability to concentrate and learn, his own feelings of happiness, and his friendships.

3. Possible answers:

   (a) Children who bully others can be negatively affected by their own behavior.

   (b) Children who are bullied at school suffer in many aspects of their lives, not just when they are at school.

Page 45

- Answers should include advice about dealing with the bullying soon and about the negative effects of the bullying, including problems sleeping, feelings of unhappiness and fear, isolation, thoughts about suicide, inability to concentrate at school, and a lack of desire to attend school.

Supporting Activity

- Students can research in depth the effects of stress and anxiety on a person's physical and mental health and present their findings in a PowerPoint™ (or similar) presentation.

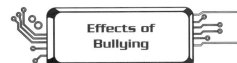

Previous 10

Jeb's blogspot

Man walks into a bar and says, "Ouch"

JANUARY 12, 2011

I've been trying not to talk much about the bully, Dean, at school in my blog because … well, it's embarrassing. But it's starting to affect my whole life, so here goes—maybe someone out there has some good advice.

It's only been happening for a couple of weeks, but it's getting to me more and more. I don't want to go to school—I'll say I'm sick, I've got a headache, whatever, anything to get out of school, even though I know my grades are falling. There's no point going anyway, I can't concentrate when I'm so stressed out about what Dean will say or do next. In the mornings, I don't even want to get out of bed—you know how I used to get up early and go for a run? Well, not anymore. I don't feel like getting up, let alone running. I just want to stay home where it's safe.

I feel depressed. My worrying means I can't sleep or eat properly. I feel sick. I feel alone and don't know who to trust. I don't know what to do, or how much more my life will change if the bullying continues. Last month I read an article about someone my age who committed suicide because he was being bullied. I don't think I could ever do that, but I totally get how he felt so bad.

Dean doesn't look like stopping, even though I can see he's not happy and his "friends" are only hanging out with him because they are too scared not to. He can't be concentrating or learning much at school while he's so busy planning how to get me. I don't know if I should do anything or what I could do. Any ideas?

—Jeb

#Comments   #Permalink   #Share   E-mail this link:

Taylah14 says:

Jeb, this is awful! It's affecting your whole life—in a bad way. Have you told anyone, like your parents? Maybe they could help you out?

There are a few help lines you can call if you think you can't tell your parents. I also know a help website. I'll put a link to that site below …

Archives

- June 2011
- May 2011
- April 2011
- March 2011
- February 2011
- January 2011
- December 2010
- November 2010

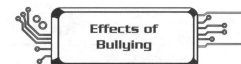

WRITE ABOUT IT

Record your answers after discussing the text on page 43.

1. Describe how the bullying is affecting Jeb's:

   (a) ability to learn at school _____

   _____

   (b) sleep _____

   _____

   (c) school attendance _____

   _____

   (d) mental and emotional well-being _____

   _____

   (e) physical health _____

   _____

   (f) daily routine _____

   _____

2. Write two ways Dean is being affected by his own behavior.

   _____

   _____

   _____

3. The following statements are false. Rewrite them to make them true.

   (a) "Children who bully others aren't affected at all by their own actions."

   _____

   _____

   _____

   (b) "A child who is bullied at school is only affected while at school."

   _____

   _____

   _____

   _____

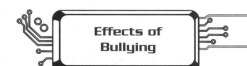

MORE ABOUT IT

Imagine your best friend has just posted this message on his or her blog:

Recent Entries | Archive | Friends | User Info | Memories

Sam's blog

So, do you like ... stuff?

Previous 10

Profile

Bad news!

I think I am being bullied. 😟

I'm kind of upset but ... it'll go away, I hope. 😐

It's probably not worth doing anything about it, is it?

Write a response to let your friend know what sort of effects the bullying might have on his or her life, and why something should be done about it sooner rather than later. Include emoticons.

It's probably not worth doing anything about it, is it? 😐

Comment:

Focus

To read about and discuss the long-term effects of bullying

Teacher Information

- Sometimes the effects of bullying last long into adulthood. Adults who were targets of childhood bullying can have low self-esteem, have difficulty making and maintaining friendships, suffer from depression, be unable to fulfill their academic potential, have poor career prospects, be open to bullying in the workplace, engage in self-harm, attempt suicide, plan or engage in revenge attacks, and be involved in abusive behavior at home.

- For the bully, long-term effects can include unpopularity and loss of peer group because "friends" no longer fear retribution, continued antisocial behavior possibly leading to crime, and abusive behavior.

- One researcher, Dan Olweus, found in his studies that being a target of bullying in Grades 6 and 9 could be linked to greater depression and lower self-esteem at 23 years of age. Olweus also noticed a connection between bullying and later criminality, with 60% of those who identified themselves as bullies in Grades 6 and/or 9 having at least one criminal conviction by age 24 (Olweus, 1993).

Introduction

- If possible, complete the section on the short-term effects of bullying (pages 42–45) before completing this section. Recall the bully, Dean, and the effects the bullying was having on both Dean and Jeb, the target of the bullying. If students did not complete the previous activity, quickly discuss the short-term effects of bullying as outlined in the teacher's information on page 42. Briefly introduce the two characters, Dean (bully) and Jeb (target).

Discussing the Text

- What effects has the bullying had on Jeb's life as an adult? (The bullying at school has affected Jeb's ability to make friends and his mental health, self-esteem, and confidence.)

- What happened to Dean in school that might have contributed to him becoming a bully? (Dean was bullied before becoming a bully himself.)

- What could have been some consequences of Jeb dropping out of school, especially on his career chances? (Jeb dropping out of school means he perhaps didn't reach his full academic potential, so he wasn't able to continue learning or get a good job.)

Answers

Page 47

Children who *bully* others may be more likely to:
- Have alcohol/and or drug issues
- Have a criminal conviction for stealing, vandalism, or assault
- Have difficulty maintaining friendships
- Continue to be aggressive.

Children who are *bullied* may:
- Become bullies themselves
- Suffer from depression
- Have poor self-esteem or self-confidence
- Drop out of school
- Have social problems such as difficulty making friends.

Supporting Activity

- In pairs, the students can role-play being someone who goes back in time to tell 10-year-old Dean or Jeb the effects the bullying will have on them.

Reference

Olweus, D. (1993) *Bullying at School: What We Know and What We Can Do.* Blackwell, Cambridge, MA.

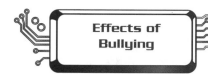
The Bully and the Victim—20 Years Later

READ ABOUT IT

 Springfield Psychology Service—Appointment Book

Tuesday, 5 p.m.

Client name: Jeb Thomas

Age: 30

Reason for referral:

Depression

Low self-esteem, poor self-confidence

Social problems

Difficulty making friends

Background notes:

Was bullied at school for a prolonged period by a child named Dean King.

Left school early.

Thursday, 6 p.m.

Client name: Dean King

Age: 30

Reason for referral:

Aggressive tendencies

Difficulty maintaining friendships

Issues with drugs and alcohol since late teens

Background notes:

Was bullied in elementary school, then became a bully himself in middle and high school.

Spent time in prison for vandalism, stealing, and assault.

WRITE ABOUT IT

The consequences of bullying can be damaging and long lasting for both the bully and the target, long after the bullying has stopped.

Write at least three possible long-term effects of bullying on the bully and the target.

Children who *bully others* may be more likely to:	Children who *are bullied* may:

MORE ABOUT IT

Imagine your friend is bullying someone. Write what you could say to your friend to help him or her understand the possible long-term effects of such actions on the target's life.

_____

_____

_____

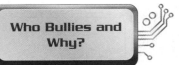
Focus

To read and discuss a cartoon strip about bullying (in which a humiliating cell phone image is forwarded) to identify the characteristics of bullies and why they bully

Teacher Information

- *Bystander bullying* is of particular relevance to cyberbullying. Refer to page *viii* for further information about bystander bullying. Students may pass on images or information concerning a target that amuses or shocks them without thinking about or being aware of the effect on the target and of their own role as bullies.

- Depending on the nature of the material being sent, students forwarding information may unconsciously be performing an illegal act.

- There can be no one set of characteristics to describe all bullies. A bully may be a very confident, high-achieving, and apparently popular student with high self-esteem. Bullying is usually about power and control.

Bullies may:

- Be impulsive, socially dominant
- Lack empathy and sympathy
- Be able to talk their way out of trouble
- Be confident and popular
- Have a small group of friends who support their bullying.

Reasons for bullying:

- Having fun at the expense of others
- To demonstrate technological expertise

Introduction

- Students need to understand that forwarding hurtful information they receive is a form of bullying.

Discussing the Text

- Why do you think the boys sent the image to Cal? (Answers may include: He looked different. He got upset. They thought he wouldn't know they sent it. He was bigger and stronger than they were. They thought it was funny. They wanted to show they were clever and could change the picture.)

- Why was Cal so upset? (Answers may include: He knew people were laughing. The picture looked like him. He was embarrassed and angry. He didn't know what to do about it.)

Answers

Page 50

1. (a) smaller
   (b) it was fun
   (c) is very clever at using
   (d) didn't think
   (e) had
   (f) are
   (g) knew

2. Teacher check

3. (a) true   (b) true   (c) false   (d) true
   (e) true   (f) false   (g) true   (h) true
   (i) true

Page 51

Teacher check

Supporting Activity

- Make a list of reasons why bullies like Sam and Taj use chat rooms and cell phones to bully instead of bullying physically.

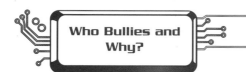
READ ABOUT IT

The next day

Taj: "Look Sam, now it really does look like it's Cal taking a shower."

Sam: "It sure does. This will be the best thing we've done to him, and he won't know it was us. I'll forward it to everyone for a laugh. You'll have to show me how you do it."

Mom: "What did you do?"

Cal: "I just deleted it, of course. I don't know who sent it, but I bet Sam had something to do with it."

Dad: "That's just what you don't do. You need to keep the evidence. We'll have to tell the school about this."

Cal: "But Dad, I don't want anyone else to see it. You could see everything! It was really gross."

Dad: "Cal, it's not you in the photo, and these bullies have to be stopped."

WRITE ABOUT IT

Record your answers after discussing the text on page 49.

1. Underline the best words to complete each sentence.

   (a) Sam and Taj are bigger/smaller than their target.

   (b) The boys bullied Cal because it was fun/he deserved it.

   (c) Taj is very clever at using/doesn't know much about cell phones.

   (d) The bullies thought/didn't think Cal would know who changed the picture.

   (e) The boys had/hadn't bullied Cal before.

   (f) The students who forwarded the picture are/aren't also bullying Cal.

   (g) The children knew/didn't know their actions would hurt Cal.

2. (a) What do you think the other students think about Taj?

   _____

   _____

   _____

   _____

   (b) Design a poster. Include a picture of Taj or Sam on your poster with a description of what he looks like and what he did to be called a bully.

   WANTED FOR BULLYING

   NAME:

   DESCRIPTION:

3. Write true or false after each statement about bullies.

   (a) Cyberbullies believe that no one will know who did it.

   (b) Some very clever people are bullies.

   (c) All bullies are bigger and stronger than their targets.

   (d) People who forward hurtful things that other people have sent them are bullies.

   (e) Bullies really want to hurt people.

   (f) Bullies have a great sense of humor.

   (g) Most bullies are sad, unhappy people.

   (h) Many bullies are popular people.

   (i) People are scared of bullies.

MORE ABOUT IT

1. (a) Have you or one of your friends ever received or heard about a text message that was a form of bullying? | Yes | | No |

(b) Describe the person who sent it. _____

_____

_____

(c) Why do you think this person sent the message?

_____

_____

_____

(d) Write a text message you could send back to a bully who sent you something unkind.

_____

_____

_____

There are many different types of bullies. Some bullies:

- *are big and powerful and physically hurt others*
- *are sneaky and bully by not letting others feel part of a group*
- *are jealous of what other people have, and take, hide, or damage their property*
- *make fun of others and make them feel bad*
- *are confident, popular leaders, while others are the opposite*
- *become bullies because they don't want a bully to pick on them, too.*

2. (a) Discuss bullies with a partner and decide which type you think is the worst.

The worst type of bully is: _____

(b) Make a list of some of the things this type of bully does, reasons why he or she does it, and how you think this type of bully can be helped or stopped.

Bullying behaviors	Possible reasons	Helping/Stopping this bully

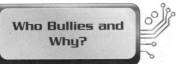

Focus

To read and discuss a play about bullying by exclusion to identify the characteristics of bullies and reasons for their bullying

Teacher Information

- Bullies may:
  - ~ be socially dominant and need to control
  - ~ lack empathy and sympathy
  - ~ create a small, tightly knit group of friends who support their bullying
  - ~ be likely to use social exclusion if they are girls.

- Reasons for bullying
  - ~ they find their targets annoying
  - ~ it is enjoyable
  - ~ to feel superior
  - ~ to feel powerful and in control
  - ~ overly permissive parenting and lack of limits

Refer to page *viii* for further information.

Introduction

- Students should realize that bullying is a deliberate act but one that not all bullies will admit to. Girls who bully by exclusion are likely to try to deny or attempt to justify their actions.

Discussing the Text

- How do you think their teacher knew the girls were bullying Claire? (Answers may include: He could see the upset look on her face. He heard what they said. He saw them walk away and leave her. He'd seen them laughing at Claire. He knew they spent a lot of time whispering together.)

- Make a list of possible comments the bullies could have made if accused of bullying Claire. (Answers may include: We didn't hurt her. She always makes things up about us. She is always sad. She doesn't like the same things we do. She is different. She's pathetic. She is always wanting to hang around us. She just doesn't get the message we don't like her. She's just a drama queen!)

Answers

Page 54

1. (a) They were trying to make her feel left out and sad.

   (b) Yes. They deliberately talked about shopping and didn't tell her it was for the party.

   (c) No. They wouldn't have treated her that way if they cared.

2. Claire didn't share their interest in clothes and wasn't allowed to wear makeup. She tried to be nice to the bullies and got upset when they were unkind to her.

3. Teacher check

4. (a) They thought they were better than their target and enjoyed bullying her. They thought it was fun.

   (b) No. Targets of bullying are never to blame for being bullied.

Page 55

Teacher check

Supporting Activities

- Work in a small group to write a play script set in Mr. Tan's office in which he talks to the girls, asks them questions, and tries to help them and make sure they stop bullying.

- Write an acrostic from a target's point of view using the letters of the word EXCLUDED as the beginning letters.

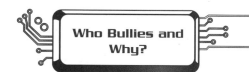
READ ABOUT IT

Bree: What are you going to wear to my party?

Kate: Mom said I can get a new top, and I'll just wear my straight-leg jeans.

Ling: I've got some new really short shorts and a purple top.

Bree: Do you two want to come shopping with me on Saturday? I have some birthday money to spend and we could look at makeup, too.

Kate: Mom might let me buy my new top then, too!

Ling: Shh! Here's Claire. Don't let her hear about our plans, or she'll want to come, too.

Bree: She's so not into clothes. Did you see what she wore when we went to the movies for Rachel's birthday? And her mom won't even let her wear any makeup.

(They all laugh.)

Claire: Hi! What's so funny?

Ling: *(Shaking her head)* Nothing.

Claire: Have you finished your lunch yet?

Kate: Yes, we were just talking about things.

Claire: What things?

Ling: Just things.

Bree: Like my birthday next week.

Claire: What are you doing for it?

Bree: Nothing much.

Kate: I've got some really great shoes I can wear. They look good with my jeans. What shoes are you going to wear, Ling?

Ling: I have some black boots.

Bree: If I have enough money left, I'll look at new shoes on Saturday.

Claire: What are they for?

Bree: Just to wear.

Ling: How are you going to wear your hair, Bree?

Bree: I think I'll wear it up if I can. My sister said she'd do it for me.

Kate: You're so lucky! Your sister is wonderful.

Claire: My sister got on the state basketball team.

(The three girls ignore her comment, stand up, and walk off. Claire looks sadly after them and stays seated.)

WRITE ABOUT IT

Record your answers after discussing the text on page 51.

1. (a) What were the three girls trying to do to Claire?

_____

_____

_____

(b) Do you think they knew how they were making her feel? | **Yes** | **No** |

Explain why you think this. _____

_____

_____

(c) Do you think any of them cared about her feelings? | **Yes** | **No** |

Why/Why not? _____

_____

2. Why did the bullies choose Claire as their target?

_____

_____

_____

3. Which of the three girls do you think was the worst bully?

Why? _____

_____

_____

There are many reasons why people bully others. Some are bullies because they are jealous. Others bully because it makes them feel strong and powerful. Some bully because they are unhappy and dissatisfied with their own lives, others because they think they are better than their target. Some just enjoy it and think it's fun.

4. (a) Why do you think these girls were bullying?

_____

_____

(b) Do you think Claire was to blame in any way? | **Yes** | **No** |

Why/Why not? _____

_____

_____

MORE ABOUT IT

Imagine the girls' teacher had overheard their conversation and told them they were being very unkind and were in fact bullying Claire. He said they had to write him a letter explaining what they had done, why they had done it, and what they were going to do in the future.

(a) Choose to be one of the girls, think about her reaction to being called a bully, and write her letter to Mr. Tan.

```



```

(b) Write one comment or piece of advice you think Mr. Tan might give the girl after reading the letter.

_____

_____

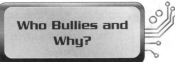

Focus

To read and discuss a report about physical bullying to identify the characteristics of bullies and reasons for their bullying

Teacher Information

- Bullying is generally about power and control.
- Bullies may:
  - ~ be impulsive, socially dominant, easily frustrated, confrontational, and aggressive
  - ~ have a conduct disorder
  - ~ question authority, break rules, push boundaries, admire violence
  - ~ be able to talk their way out of trouble
  - ~ create a small, tightly knit group of friends who support their bullying
  - ~ be physically bigger and stronger than their targets.
- Reasons for bullying
  - ~ jealousy and competition for attention and valued objects
  - ~ to feel superior
  - ~ to feel powerful and in control
  - ~ to show how tough they are

Introduction

- Students will need to be familiar with the concept of *bystanders* being those who observe bullying. Bystanders become accessories to bullying when they encourage bullying by, for example, making statements of support, laughing, or jeering. Even passive bystanders who observe bullying and fail to take any action are themselves, by definition, bullies. (Refer to page *viii* for further information.)
- There is another distinct category of individuals involved with bullying—*advocates:* those who may have been told something about the bullying, or suspected it was happening, but haven't actually witnessed it. They're not bystanders, accessories, bullies, or targets. (Refer to page *viii* for further information.)

Discussing the Text

- Discuss the people mentioned in the report, what they did or saw, what you think they should have done, and how their behavior might change in the future as a result of this report.
- What is the value of a teacher writing a bullying report? Give reasons for and against writing a report like this one.

Answers

Page 59

1. Troy Browning. No. He didn't see the bullying happening.

   Tom Anderson. No. He wanted to help, but didn't get a chance.

   Tran Hu. Yes. He was an accessory. He didn't admit Trent bullied Ben and tried to justify the bullying.

   Trent Way. Yes. He admitted bullying and tried to blame Ben.

   Jack Walker. Yes. He was a bystander bully. He admitted bullying and tried to justify it.

2. Ben isn't popular, is weak, clumsy, not good at sports, a show-off, is given lots of great things, and makes others feel bad.

3. (a) Possible answers include: He may not be looked after by his parents; e.g., having to steal lunch because he was hungry. He may not get many things from his parents. He may be from a poor background.

   (b) No. Jack and Tran did not feel sorry for Ben. Jack said Trent (the bully) was only having fun. Tran called Ben "a wimp."

4. (a) bossy, cruel, a leader, unkind, popular, jealous, clever, happy

   (b) Teacher check

   (c) Teacher check

Supporting Activity

- Work in a small group to role-play the teacher interviewing one of the people involved in this bullying.

READ ABOUT IT

Report written by:	Philip White – Grade 6 teacher
Bullying reported by:	Mr. and Mrs. Tavistock (parents), Josh Taylor (Grade 6 student)
Date(s):	February 22, February 24, March 1
Time(s):	After school and at lunchtime
Location(s):	School playground
Target(s):	Ben Tavistock
Bully/Bullies:	Trent Way
Bystanders/Accessories:	Jack Walker, Tom Anderson, Tran Hu

Target's Report:

Trent has been picking on me all term, usually after school but sometimes at lunchtime, too. He calls me names and takes my things and won't give them back. Sometimes he puts them in hard-to-get-at places, like on top of a wall. Last Monday, he took the special pen that Dad bought me in Hong Kong and I haven't got it back. I didn't tell Dad because I knew he'd be really angry. On Wednesday, Trent took my lunch and ate it, and last Monday he tripped me up on the way home from school. I fell and cut my head on some rocks. It was bleeding so badly Mom made me tell her what had happened.

Bystanders and "Accessories" Reports:

Jack Walker

On Wednesday, I saw Trent take Ben's lunch, but Ben wasn't eating it and he didn't even look hungry. Trent told him to come and get it back if he wanted it, but he didn't. Trent was only having fun, and he was starving because his mom didn't give him any lunch.

Tom Anderson

Last Monday after school, I saw Ben fall down and cut his head on some rocks. He was walking past Trent when it happened. I didn't see Trent actually do anything to Ben, but Trent, Tran, and Jack laughed and laughed and did high fives. I knew Ben was hurt. After they left, I was going over to help him but he took off. I could see he was bleeding a lot.

Tran Hu

Last Monday, Ben said that Trent took his pen. I didn't see Trent take it. Ben is such a wimp, and he's always blaming Trent for doing things. Ben always has lots of really good stuff his dad gets him when he's traveling. He's always showing off about what he has and making other people feel bad. He wouldn't stop talking about his stupid pen and showing it to everyone.

Bully's Report:

I am always getting into trouble for things I've done to Ben. He isn't very popular, none of the kids like him, and he's really weak. He's clumsy and hopeless at sports, and the boys don't want to play with him. He's a show-off and gets all this stuff he keeps boasting about and showing people. He makes other people feel bad. He doesn't deserve to have more than we do.

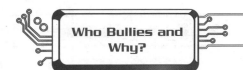

READ ABOUT IT (continued)

Other Reports:

Parents

Ben has been very unhappy at school, and unexplained things keep happening to him. He keeps losing things, or he brings them home damaged. He won't talk about what's happening, but we've been very worried about him. He had some friends at school last year, but he doesn't seem to do anything with them now. He just sits at home and plays on his computer. He's been very lonely, and he seemed scared. When he came home very upset and bleeding last night and said he wasn't going to school today, we knew it was serious. We made him tell us what was happening and—Trent and some of his followers are making his life miserable. He is also sad that his friends don't come near him anymore.

Troy Browning

I think Ben might be being bullied by some of the boys in our class, but I haven't seen it happen. Some of them laugh when he has to come to the front of the class and do something, and they have said things I couldn't hear. I heard that he was hurt last night because Trent tripped him.

Action Taken:

Ben has been interviewed and told that bullying will not be tolerated by this school and that he will be offered support by staff and students. He must report any further incidents immediately.

Bullying has been discussed in class, and the role played by associates and bystanders as bullies has been made very clear. Students have agreed to report any bullying and to support Ben and any other targets they become aware of.

Trent and his associates have been interviewed. The differences between teasing and having fun, and bullying, have been made very clear to them. Trent is a confident leader who is good at rationalizing his behavior and making excuses. It will not be easy for him to accept that he is a bully and to realize that there will be consequences if he continues to target other less powerful students. He must return the pen and tell Ben he is sorry he was hurt.

Trent's parents were interviewed. After looking at the information collected in this report and some further discussion, they reluctantly accepted that some of Trent's behavior was unacceptable and in the future they would be less prepared to believe his version of all events. They reported that he has always been bigger and stronger than many of his peers and is proud of this and generally has a poor opinion of weakness in any form.

Monitoring in Place:

Bullying will be discussed in class regularly and follow-up interviews of all of the students conducted in two weeks' time.

Ben's and Trent's parents will be informed of any positive changes in behavior or if any further bullying occurs.

Who Bullies and Why?

WRITE ABOUT IT

Record your answers after discussing the reports on pages 57 and 58.

1. Who is a bully? Write yes or no after each name and explain your answer.

Name	Bully?	Why/Why not
Troy Browning		
Tom Anderson		
Tran Hu		
Trent Way		
Jack Walker		

2. Trent thought it was okay to bully Ben. List two of the reasons Trent used to justify bullying Ben.

    - _____
    - _____

3. (a) Why do you think Trent became a bully?

    _____

    _____

    (b) Do you think Jack and Tran felt sorry for Ben? Explain your answer.

    _____

    _____

MORE ABOUT IT

brave	strong	bossy	helpful	cruel	a leader	caring
unkind	popular	weak	jealous	clever	sorry	happy

4. (a) Circle the words above that **you** would use to describe Trent.

    (b) Not all bullies are the same. Underline the words you would use to describe a bully you know.

    (c) What is the main difference between this bully and Trent?

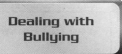

Focus

To read and discuss a poem describing the feelings of a target approaching a group of bullies

Teacher Information

- Many children experience bullying to a greater or lesser degree. Bullies thrive on the emotional reaction of their targets, be it anger, fear, or tears. Targets who escape lightly have possibly not given the bullies sufficient reaction to make it worth their while pursuing them.

- Confident children with a positive self-image may be able to dismiss their bullies naturally, but others need to be given strategies to deal positively with them. Sufficiently armed, children are empowered to take a stand against bullies and are less likely to be regular targets in the future.

- Refer to page *ix* for further information.

Introduction

- The poem describes the feelings of a child as she finds her way blocked by bullies. She considers changing her route rather than confronting them, but realizes that this is running away from the problem. She has a strategy for coping and knows that she must show the courage and determination needed to carry it out. Her positive body language, eye contact, and bright smile stun her bullies, leaving them speechless. They were expecting an emotional response. As she walks away, she feels that she has conquered her problem.

Discussing the Text

- Who is the "I" in the poem? (A target)

- What is her first instinct? (To run away, find an alternate route)

- Why does she stay? (She has a solution that she is determined to carry out.)

- Is this strategy natural or learned? (Direct discussion that leads the students to the conclusion that although the poem does not specify, her initial fear indicates that it is learned rather than natural.)

- If learned, from whom? (The poem does not specify, but the students should be led to the conclusion that the target learned the strategy from someone in whom she has confided—a friend, teacher, parent, or other adult.)

- What is the key thing to remember in such a situation? (Do not show any concern. Do not react emotionally.)

- Why is reporting bullying incidents so important? (To share your worries and discover ways for dealing with them; to help in the eradication of bullying)

- If a target employs such strategies, not only will he or she be a less likely target in the future but also … (his or her confidence and self-esteem will increase to the point that protective strategies will be employed naturally).

Answers

1. target

2. The writer sees her bullies and considers taking an alternate route but decides against it, knowing that she must stand up to them.

3. determined

4. because of the way she looks, her hair, and the clothes she wears

5. She shows them that their taunts don't bother her. She walks by confidently, having made eye contact and given them a friendly smile.

6. Answers may include: elation at having successfully silenced her bullies and relief that she managed to hide her fear from them.

Supporting Activity

- Create large "anti-bullying flowers" for display in which a bullying situation is placed in the center and the possible strategies for coping with it are placed as petals around it.

READ ABOUT IT

They're waiting there. What shall I do?
Maybe walk a different way?
NO! I have a solution.
I must follow it through.

My shoulders go back. I will walk tall.
I look straight ahead.
They will NOT see my fear.

As I approach, I hear them jeer.
The way I look, my clothes, my hair.
I turn to face them, eye to eye.
A friendly smile lights up my face.

They look confused. What have I done?
Expecting fear or anger, they stand, struck dumb.
I do not stop. I do not speak.
I keep on walking, my battle won.

WRITE ABOUT IT

1. The poem is written by a ⌨target ⌨bully .

2. Describe what is happening in verse 1.

_____

_____

3. Rearrange the letters to find a word describing how the writer feels in verse 2.

     d   d   e   e   e   i   m   n   r   t

_____

4. Why is the target being bullied? _____

5. How does the target silence the bullies? _____

_____

6. How do you think the writer feels as she walks past her bullies? _____

_____

MORE ABOUT IT

Do you know of anyone, including yourself or a character in a story, who has been in the writer's situation?
Write a poem in the first person, describing either how the situation was dealt with or how it could have been
dealt with better. Use the back of the worksheet.

Focus

To read and discuss a dialogue between friends in which one helps the other realize that he has the ability to deal with bullying

Teacher Information

- To persist with bullying a certain person or group, bullies rely on evoking a reaction in them. They want to see fear, hurt, and anger in their targets because these responses give them the feeling of power on which they thrive. By learning strategies to deal positively with bullying attacks, students are empowered to take a stand against bullies and are less likely to be regular targets in the future.

- Refer to page *ix* for further information.

Introduction

- In the text, Zac is explaining to Goran that bullies are people who feel the need to assert themselves in a negative way because they are unhappy or uncomfortable with some aspect of their lives. The problem belongs to the bully and not to the target, a concept that many targets find hard to believe. Taking on the role of bully soothes their egos, giving them a sense of power that somehow compensates for the imbalance in their lives.

- By being assertive and constantly reaffirming one's self-worth, a target can develop the confidence to stand up to bullies and respond to them in a way that will stop the bullying.

- On page 65, students look at possible responses to a bully's taunts. Positive responses are intended to stop the bully, not to provoke him or her. Ideal responses include those that: agree with the bully, make light of the intended insults, are noncommittal or vague.

Discussing the Text

- Before listening to what Zac has to say, Goran has already taken the first step to defeat the bullies. What is it? (Talking to someone about the bullying)

- Why is it useful to have a mantra? (Positive, confidence building, an affirmation of self-worth)

- Why do you need to know that it is the bully who has the problem? (By understanding the bully's weakness, you may halt the bullying.)

- Why do some bullies pretend to be someone they're not? (So they can forget their real lives and the problems they may have.)

- What are some ways to assert yourself and not be a target? (Look and move confidently. Smile. Relax.)

- Can you only look confident if you feel that way? (You may feel very nervous and afraid, but you can pretend to be confident and, with practice, you will be.)

- Is it cheating to have a script ready in case of bullying? (It's good to be prepared and to have an idea of what to say in a situation in which you may be feeling worried and unable to think clearly.)

Answers

Page 64

1. I am not to blame. No one has the right to bully me. I have the right to be safe from bullying.

2. Zac believes Goran needs to understand that it is the bullies who have the problem and not the targets. It will help Zac understand that it is not his fault.

3. When you're being someone else, you don't have to worry about any problems you have in the real world.

4. Positive self-talk and body language: eye contact, head up, shoulders back, relaxed face, speak strongly and clearly, stay calm, walk away confidently.

5. Even though Goran will be asserting himself, on the inside he will be feeling very nervous and even scared.

6. You don't have to think of a response at a time when you might be feeling flustered and unable to think clearly.

Page 65

For exchanges A–D, Target 2 gives the positive responses.

Supporting activity

Compose and role-play a number of exchanges with both emotional and positive responses. Analyze the body language and movements of the bully and the target in each exchange.

READ ABOUT IT

Zac is chatting online with his younger cousin, Goran.

Zac - Conversation

| Photos | Files | Video | Call | Games | Activities | >> |

Zac: How are you, dude? Haven't heard from you in a while!

Goran: It's not fair! Why am I always being pushed around and made fun of?

Zac: Ah, so you're being bullied. D'you know what? It's not your problem. It's theirs.

Goran: How do you figure that?

Zac: Think about it … if you're happy with your life and you've got a good balance between work and play, family and friends, why would you be unkind to anyone?

Goran: Well, I wouldn't, I suppose.

Zac: Exactly! Kids who bully have a huge problem. Something about their lives is unbalanced and they feel the need to hit out in some way.

Goran: I never really thought about it like that. But the kids who bully me are smart, good at sports, popular … what could be wrong with their lives?

Zac: Life's complicated and things aren't always as they seem. Playing the bully can be a front for people who are not comfortable with who they really are. You wouldn't believe the number of famous actors who took to the stage because they were painfully shy. It's much easier pretending to be someone else than being yourself.

Goran: That helps me to understand why it's their problem and not mine, but how does it help me deal with the bullies?

Zac: You must remember a few key points: You are not to blame. No one has the right to bully you. You have the right to be safe from bullying. This is your mantra. Repeat it now, and show me that you really believe it.

Goran: I am not to blame. No one has the right to bully me. I have the right to be safe from bullying.

Zac: Excellent! Remember to repeat it silently whenever you feel threatened. So, what are you going to do the next time you are confronted by a bully?

Goran: I'll repeat the mantra in my head … calmly … then I'll … I'll … I'm not sure. I just don't know how to handle it … I mean, what would I actually do?

Zac: OK. First step, repeat your mantra. Second step is eye contact. Look your aggressor straight in the eye. Let him or her speak. Stand tall, head up, shoulders back, and maintain eye contact. Keep your face relaxed so that you look calm.

Goran: Then what?

Zac: Now it's your turn to "take to the stage." On the inside, you'll be feeling wobbly like jelly. But in a strong, clear voice, you're going to speak calmly, still looking, then turn and stride away confidently with your head up and shoulders back.

Goran: I can see that might work, but there's just one thing missing … the script!

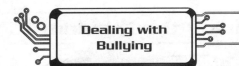
WRITE ABOUT IT

Record your answers after discussing the text on page 63.

1. A mantra is a repetitive phrase that can help to give inner peace or strength.
   Write the mantra suggested by Zac.

I am not to blame. No one has the right to bully me. I have the right to be safe from bullying.

2. Why does Zac take the time to explain why he thinks bullies bully?

3. What does Zac mean when he says, "It's much easier pretending to be someone else than being yourself"?

4. How does Zac suggest ways in which Goran should assert himself when confronted by bullies?

5. What does Zac mean when he says, "On the inside, you'll be feeling wobbly like jelly"?

6. Why is it a good idea to have a script of prepared responses to deliver when you find yourself in a bullying situation?

MORE ABOUT IT

Bullies thrive on the reactions of their targets. One who gets upset, angry, or shows fear gives the bully so much pleasure and satisfaction that he or she is going to offend that target over and over again.

1. Read each exchange between a bully and two targets.
   - Highlight the positive response that will stop the bully from coming back.
   - Write another positive target response for each.

   A. Bully: Hey, Beanpole! What's it like up there in the stratosphere?

   Target 1: Stop calling me names! It's not my fault I'm much taller than everyone else!

   Target 2: Well, on a clear day, I can see as far as the ocean.

   _____

   _____

   _____

   B. Bully: Here she comes … Phew! What a dreadful smell!

   Target 1: Don't be so mean! I don't smell! I shower twice a day.

   Target 2: Yes, isn't it awful! I was conned at the market. They said it was Chanel No. 5!

   _____

   _____

   _____

   C. Bully: So tomorrow, you bring me your lunch and don't forget, or else!

   Target 1: That's not fair! I can't bring two lunches. What will I have to eat?

   Target 2: I'm happy to give away Dad's famous veggie loaf. You'll be doing me a favor!

   _____

   _____

   _____

   D. Bully: Don't try to tackle me on the field, Squirt, or you'll get what you deserve!

   Target 1: OK. I'll keep out of your way, but please don't hurt me.

   Target 2: Of course not! You're so good at the game, I could never compete with you.

   _____

   _____

   _____

2. Compose and role-play an exchange with both emotional and positive responses.

Focus

To read and discuss a selection of strategies to deal with bullying

Teacher Information

- To persist with bullying, bullies rely on evoking a reaction in their targets. They want to see fear, hurt, or anger. These responses give bullies the feeling of power on which they thrive. By learning strategies to deal positively with bullying attacks, students are empowered to stand up for themselves and are less likely to be regular targets in the future.

- Refer to page *ix* for further information.

Introduction

- The discussion text begins with a short exposition about an individual's right to a bully-free existence. There are many students with low self-esteem who will need to be convinced that this includes them.

  The exposition ends with a strong statement suggesting that everyone has a proactive role to play in working towards the eradication of bullying.

- The commands suggest ways for targets to deal with bullying, helping them to stand up to bullies without showing signs of emotion. Explain that a mantra is a set of short statements; in this case, affirming the child's worth.

- The way the commands are presented suggests that support for targets of bullying can be found all around.

- Traditionally, students have been uncomfortable with the idea of informing on a bully, not only through fear but also because it can be seen as a sign of weakness. Students need to understand that it is not only acceptable to report bullying but it is essential. Most would have no hesitation in reporting a crime because they know it's against the law and therefore must be wrong. If they know bullying is wrong, they should understand that reporting it is just as important.

- In the activity on page 69, students suggest the ten most effective ways to deal with bullying situations.

Discussing the Text

- Why should we try to end bullying? (No one has the right to make anyone else miserable, scared, or angry.)

- How does a bully choose his or her targets? (Nervous people look like they will respond the way the bully wants, while confident people don't.)

- Why should you never show an emotional response? (That's what the bully wants.)

- How can a target limit the isolating effects of exclusion by peers? (By joining in with other activities, making an effort to be friendly to everyone)

- Is cyberbullying as anonymous as some bullies think? (Text and e-mails can be traced.)

- How can you stop the spread of nasty Internet messages? (Don't forward them.)

- What can bystanders do to support targets of bullying? (Listen, let them join in, confront the bullies.)

Answers

Page 68

1. Bullying is wrong. No one should stop us from being happy and feeling safe. We must do what we can to stop bullies.

2. Confident: shoulders back, head up, smiling, looking happy

   Nervous: hunched shoulders, looking down, frowning, looking scared or worried

3. Show no emotional response. Let them know that what they say or do does not bother you.

4. Find friends who accept you as you are. Take part in different activities to make more friends.

5. (a) to save evidence: to show what has been said about you; to help catch the person who sent it

   (b) not to forward text and e-mails: to stop spreading nasty perceptions about others; to show support for the target

6. By listening to them, letting them join in with their activities, telling bullies that what they're doing is unkind and asking how would they like it

7. Teacher check

Page 69

Teacher check

Supporting Activity

- Design a poster encouraging people to extend their social circle by taking part in different activities.

Dealing with Bullying

READ ABOUT IT

You all have the right to live, study, and work in an environment where you feel confident, safe, and respected. No one has the right to have the power over you to make you feel scared, miserable, or worthless. Bullying in any form is unacceptable. It is wrong. It must be stopped. It can be stopped.

The power is in all of you to stop bullying.

MILKY

If you witness any **BULLYING** support the target. Let bullies know you do not agree with what they are doing.

Believe in your right to be respected. Compose a mantra that is meaningful to you.

Practice talking clearly and confidently to friends and family. This will help you when you speak to bullies.

Walk confidently with shoulders back and head held high. Lose your frown and your fears and worries will go, too. Look and feel happier with a smile.

Respond to bullies calmly. Ask them to stop. Agree with what they say if it's true, but make light of it. Be polite, but let them know that what they say or do does not bother you. Show no emotional reaction—this is what they are looking for!

IF SOMEONE SENDS YOU UNPLEASANT TEXT MESSAGES OR E-MAILS, OR POSTS SOMETHING OFFENSIVE ON AN INTERNET CHAT OR SOCIAL NETWORK SITE, SAVE THE EVIDENCE IN A SPECIAL FOLDER. TELL AN ADULT IMMEDIATELY.

If you are being excluded, seek out the company of peers who accept you as you are. Get involved in different activities to increase your social circle. Be pleasant. Make the effort to join in and take an interest in others.

If you are being physically hurt or threatened, report the incidents immediately. Give details of all the people involved—bullies and witnesses.

If bullying persists, tell someone. You are not alone. Others will be in the same situation. You can support each other. Adults and your peers will also support you. If you keep quiet, the bullying will continue.

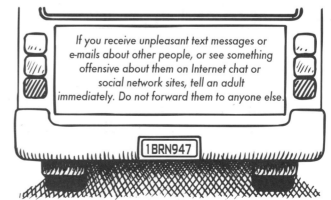

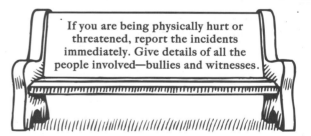

If you receive unpleasant text messages or e-mails about other people, or see something offensive about them on Internet chat or social network sites, tell an adult immediately. Do not forward them to anyone else.

1BRN947

WRITE ABOUT IT

ANTI-BULLYING MAN

Record your answers after discussing the text on page 67.

1. Write the message from the introduction as you would explain it to a younger student.

2. Complete the table by describing how the different types of people look and act.

Confident	Nervous

3. Even though being bullied can make you feel awful, what is the secret to stop bullies from targeting you?

4. What steps can you take to stop feeling sad and lonely when peers exclude you?

5. Why is it important ...

(a) to save evidence of cyberbullying?	(b) not to forward text and e-mails about others?

6. How can a witness to bullying support the target?

7. Do you agree that it is important to report bullying? Explain your answer.

MORE ABOUT IT

Bullies are people just like you.
They have no super powers or magical forces working on their side.
It is the fear and distress shown by their targets that feed their power.
They can be overcome if everyone shows them that their behavior is unacceptable.

In your own words, write a set of ten rules for dealing with bullying.

- Use a combination of your own ideas and those from page 67.
- Write them in order, listing what you believe to be the most important at the top.

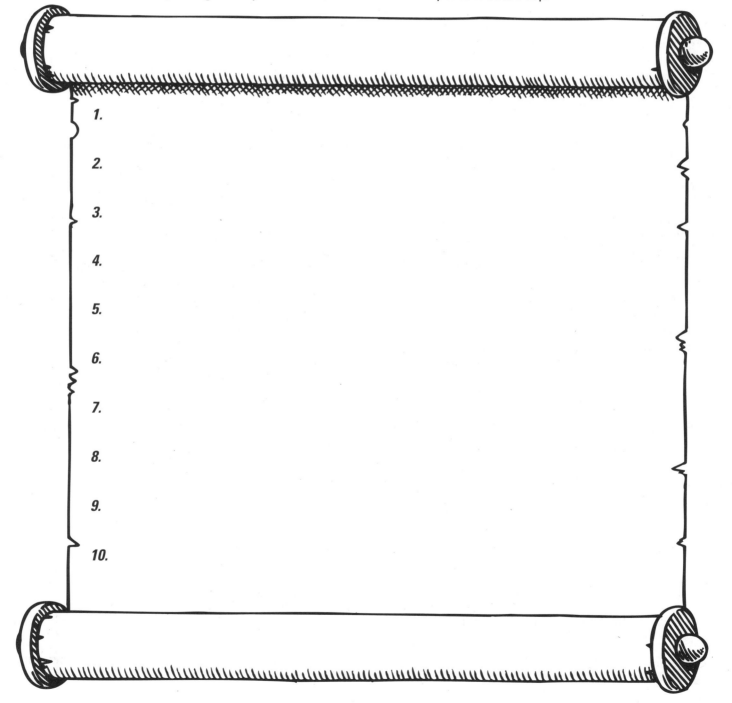

1.

2.

3.

4.

5.

6.

7.

8.

9.

10.

Focus

To read and discuss speech bubbles with diverse comments about the best ways to stop bullying at school, with a particular focus on the need to report bullying and to develop a school bullying policy

Teacher Information

- Bullying is not a new problem or one that all teachers see the same need to deal with, some perhaps because they perceive bullying as "just a part of growing up" and something they and others have all survived. Others may believe the problem is too difficult and believe they lack the skills and training to prevent it.

- There is a great deal teachers can do to prevent bullying. They can protect targets from pain and humiliation by having strategies in place to deal with bullying. They need to ensure their students are familiar with, and have sufficient confidence in, these processes to report bullying. A shared attitude of zero tolerance and a clearly articulated set of procedures and consequences can be most effective in preventing bullying both in and out of school.

- Schools also have a role in educating students about, protecting them from, and preventing cyberbullying. This invasive form of bullying can occur at any time, at great speed, and can involve huge numbers of students. A policy of procedures, processes, and consequences needs to be in place so cyberbullying is understood and reported by students and can be dealt with by the school, parents, and, if necessary, other relevant authorities.

- In order to prevent bullying, all students need to:

  ~ empathize with targets and understand more about bullying through discussions and role-plays

  ~ accept that they have a role in supporting targets and preventing bullying

  ~ understand that it is acceptable to report bullying.

- Targets need to:

  ~ be able to identify bullying behaviors and realize that bullying is wrong

  ~ understand that it is acceptable to report bullying

  ~ know they will be listened to and that action will be taken when they report bullying

  ~ realize they are not alone and that other students understand and will help them

  ~ have strategies to employ when bullied; e.g., things they can do or say

  ~ develop a support network

  ~ appear strong and confident.

Introduction

Explain:

- Bullying is usually about power and control. One of the most effective ways to prevent bullying is to reduce a bully's ability to elicit responses that confirm his/her control and power over the target.

- Schools, bystanders, and targets themselves can do a lot to prevent bullying, especially if they work together.

Discussing the Text

- What are some of the things that would stop a bully from bullying someone? (Answers may include: knowing that others recognize bullying, don't like it, and don't want it to happen; will help the target; will report the bullying; and that the bully will have to face the consequences of bullying. If the target is strong and can't be controlled. By helping the bully with his or her problems.)

- What would help a target to stand up to a bully and not let him or her have control over the target's life? (Answers may include: Knowing that bullying is wrong; that other people care, understand, and would help and report it; and that the bully will have to face some consequences. Having some good strategies to use when bullied.)

Answers

Page 72

Teacher check

Page 73

Teacher check

Supporting Activities

- Role-play one person arguing with two others about whether it is possible to stop bullying at school.

- Brainstorm lists of do's and don't's about preventing bullying.

READ ABOUT IT

We need to make bullies feel sorry for their targets.

If you look or sound different, you'll be bullied.

I think we should work together to make a bullying policy for our school.

Telling tales on bullies is a waste of time.

If bullies were caught and really punished, they'd stop doing it.

There has never been any bullying in this school.

If we report bullies, they will be made to stop.

We need to take power and control away from bullies.

Nothing we do is going to stop bullying.

We need to think about the bullies and try to help them, too.

We need to make up some school rules about bullying.

People have always bullied others and always will. It's a part of growing up.

People who respect others who are "different" are less likely to bully.

If we decide not to tolerate any bullying, it will stop.

WRITE ABOUT IT

Record your answers after discussing the text on page 71.

1. Work with a partner to choose one statement from page 71 you strongly agree with, write it in the box, and then complete the following:

[box]

   (a) Write a brief description of a person you think could have made this statement.

   _____

   _____

   (b) Check the words you think best describe how successful it would be in stopping bullying.

   highly likely   **likely**   **unlikely**   **most unlikely**

   (c) Explain why you think this.

   _____

   _____

   _____

2. Choose one statement from page 71 you disagree with, write it in the box, and then complete the following:

[box]

   (a) Write a brief description of a person you think could have made this statement.

   _____

   _____

   (b) Check the words you think best describe how successful it would be in stopping bullying.

   highly likely   **likely**   **unlikely**   **most unlikely**

   (c) Explain why you think this.

   _____

   _____

   _____

   _____

MORE ABOUT IT

Bullying at school can only be prevented if targets and bystanders report it.

1. Read the above opinion, think about someone you've seen or know about who has been bullied, and answer the questions.

   (a) Did you or someone else report the bullying?　　　Yes　　No

   (b) Why/Why not? _____

   _____

   _____

   (c) If your school had a bullying policy and you knew exactly what was going to happen after you reported bullying, do you think it would have made a difference to what you did?　　Yes　　No

   (d) Why/Why not? _____

   _____

   _____

   (e) Do you agree with the opinion about reporting bullying? _____

   _____

   (f) Explain your answer.

   _____

   _____

2. If a school bullying policy is going to prevent bullying from happening, the policy should be discussed and written by a number of people in the school.

   (a) Read the above opinion and circle the people in this list you think should be involved in writing a school's bullying policy.

parents	students	teachers	principals	targets	bullies	bystanders
school psychologists		lunchroom supervisors			assistant principals	

   (b) Why do you think having both adults and students involved in planning a bullying policy would work well?

3. Work in a small group to make a plan to show the steps you think should be followed at school after bullying has been reported. Write your plan on a large sheet of paper and include information about who should be involved, what and when they should be told, and what they should do. Think about:

   interviewing and supporting the target　　　**interviewing the bully and bystanders who are bullies**

   what teachers, parents, other students, and the principal should do

   how the bullies should be dealt with　　　**preventing further bullying**

Focus

To read and discuss a diary about bullying to identify ways bystanders can and should intervene to prevent bullying and what the targets themselves can do to prevent further bullying

Teacher Information

- There is a great deal other students can and must do to prevent bullying and protect targets from pain and humiliation. Targets themselves can also play a significant role in preventing further bullying.

- All students need to
  - ~ empathize with targets and understand more about bullying through discussions and role-plays
  - ~ accept that they have a role in supporting targets and preventing bullying
  - ~ understand that it is acceptable to report bullying.

- Targets need to:
  - ~ be able to identify bullying behaviors and realize that bullying is wrong
  - ~ understand that it is acceptable to report bullying
  - ~ know they will be listened to and action taken when they report bullying
  - ~ realize they are not alone and that other students understand and will help them
  - ~ have strategies to employ when bullied, e.g., things they can do or say
  - ~ develop a support network
  - ~ appear strong and confident.

Introduction

- Explain that bullying is usually about power and control. One of the most effective ways to prevent bullying is to reduce a bully's ability to elicit responses confirming his/her control over the target.

Discussing the Text

- How do you know that Ella had power and control over Jenna?

- How did Crystal and her friends stop Ella from controlling what Jenna did?

Answers

Page 76

1. (a) her pencil box, lunch box, and hat
   (b) Ella and her friends probably took them.

2. (a) Teacher check
   (b) She thought she was popular and she and her friends had more fun than everyone else.
   (c) Teacher check

3. (a) Teacher check
   (b) No
   (c) Answers may indicate that Crystal was on her own and they didn't think she could do anything about it.

4. (a) Ella stopped bullying and walked away.
   (b) They made fun of Ella and her questions and laughed.
   (c) Teacher check. Possible answers include: Ella wasn't able to bully all of them. Instead of being worried by what she said, they just laughed at her. Ella didn't have any power or control over them.

Page 77

Answers will vary.

Supporting Activities

- Write some rules for your class that you think would stop any bullying from happening if everyone followed them.

- Role-play a scenario in which a group of good friends tries to help someone who is being bullied so that it doesn't happen again.

READ ABOUT IT

Tuesday: *What a horrible day it's been. When I went to get my things out of my bag, I couldn't find my pencil case. I looked everywhere. It was in my bag when I left home, but it had just disappeared. I asked Ella if she'd lend me some of her stuff, but she just looked at some of her friends and they all laughed. She has a great sense of humor. I wish I could be like her. She is very popular, and I really want to be friends with her. Crystal gave me some of her pencils so I didn't get into trouble. Ella laughed and said I should wash them first—she's so funny.*

Wednesday: *It wasn't a good day. At lunchtime I went over to have lunch with Ella and some friends. They are all the popular girls who always have the most fun. When I opened my lunch box, they all held their noses because Mom had made me tuna sandwiches. Every time they saw me all day they held their noses and laughed. I hated it, and I'm really mad at Mom. Crystal told them they were mean, but they just laughed at her, too.*

Thursday: *Today I couldn't find my lunch box. It wasn't in my bag. I think Ella and some of her friends were watching me when I went to get my lunch. They were whispering together and laughing. Crystal said she had lots of rice and I could have some. It tasted very good, but Ella said I'd get slanty eyes from eating it. Every time they saw me they pulled the corners of their eyes out. It was horrible. I wish I hadn't eaten the rice.*

Friday: *I found my lunch box. The janitor said it was in the trash can. I tried to be friends with Ella, but when I went up to where she and her friends were, they all started talking loudly and didn't listen to me. I waited around for a while, but they walked off. When I followed them, they went faster and faster so I had to run.*

Monday: *I talked to Mom on the weekend, and she said she thought I should get some new friends. But I really want to be friends with Ella. Mom said she didn't think she was a good friend. At lunchtime I couldn't find Ella so I was sitting by myself and Crystal, Kate, and Gemma came and sat with me. We were talking about a movie we wanted to see when Ella came along with her friends. They held their noses and asked what I was eating. Kate just looked at them, smiled, and said, "Her lunch."*

Then Gemma said, "Yes, it's her lunch" and laughed. Ella looked at us and then walked off.

"Bye," said Crystal, smiling, and she turned around and started talking with us about the movie again. "She really is a bully," Crystal added as Ella walked away.

Tuesday: *I had a good day today. Gemma, Crystal, Kate, and I had lunch together. They are really kind to me, they're fun, and they do interesting things. I think we'll all go skating on Sunday. At recess time my hat was missing from my bag. Kate said she thought Ella must have taken it and went up to her and told her I needed it and she had to give it back. When Ella started to laugh, Crystal told her that she was a bully and they would be reporting her. Ella stopped laughing, said my hat was under a pile of books, and that we couldn't take a joke.*

Wednesday: *I had a great day. I think Mom was right. I think Ella has learned her lesson and hopefully we've stopped her from bullying me again. I've learned a lot, too!*

Jenna

WRITE ABOUT IT

Record your answers after discussing the text on page 75.

1. (a) List some of the things Jenna lost.

_____

_____

   (b) What do you think happened to them?

_____

_____

2. (a) Write six words you would use to describe Ella. _____

_____

   (b) Why do you think Jenna wanted to be friends with Ella? _____

_____

   (c) What do you think was the worst thing Ella did to Jenna? _____

_____

3. (a) Write six words you would use to describe Crystal.

_____

_____

   (b) Did the girls stop holding their noses when Crystal said they were mean? Yes   No

   (c) Why do you think they did this?

_____

_____

4. (a) What happened when the three girls decided to support Jenna on Monday?

_____

_____

   (b) Explain what they did to stop Jenna from being bullied that day.

_____

_____

   (c) Why do you think this worked?

_____

_____

MORE ABOUT IT

1. Think about someone you know or know about who was bullied, and answer the following questions.

(a) What did the bully/bullies do? _____

_____

(b) Why do you think that person was bullied? _____

_____

(c) Were there any bystanders? [**Yes**] [**No**]   (d) Did any of them try to help? [**Yes**] [**No**]

(e) What happened? _____

_____

_____

2. Complete the sentences about the incident in Question 1.

(a) I think the bystanders may have been able to stop this bullying from taking place again if they had:

_____

_____

_____

(b) Circle the best answers. I think the target could have avoided any further bullying if he/she had:

run away	found some friends to help		told a teacher
appeared more confident		made eye contact and left	
been stronger	cried	been mean to them	avoided them
laughed at them	stood up to them	hit them	called them names

3. Why do you think reporting bullying to parents and teachers is likely to prevent it from happening again?

_____

_____

_____

4. Bystanders are often even better at preventing bullying at school than teachers and parents. Suggest some possible reasons for this.

_____

_____

_____

Focus

To read and discuss a telephone conversation about bullying to identify some of the dangers of posting personal information on a social networking site and how this type of bullying can be prevented

Teacher Information

- Schools have a key role in educating students about protecting them from and preventing cyberbullying.
  In the scenario on page 79, in the form of a telephone conversation between two boys, it is revealed that one boy and his mother are being bullied by unknown people. This bullying is a result of information posted by the boy on a social networking site. The catalyst for this bullying appears to be cultural differences, in this case the particular food enjoyed by the boy and his mother.

- In order to prevent bullying of this nature, teachers need to:

  ~ help students accept and appreciate physical, cultural, and attitudinal differences

  ~ provide opportunities for students to understand bullying and empathize through role-plays and discussions

  ~ be informed about the different forms, possibilities, and technologies involved in cyberbullying.

- All students need to
  ~ appreciate differences in cultural practices, values, physical appearance, abilities, and attitudes, including sexual orientation

  ~ be aware of the need to protect personal details when posting information in chat rooms and on networking sites.

- Targets need to:
  ~ realize they are not alone and that other students understand and will help them

  ~ keep any evidence of cyberbullying.

Introduction

- Students should understand that information they post on a social networking site can be accessible to many others and that there are people who can use this information to identify them and make their lives difficult.

Discussing the Text

- How did the bully/bullies find Lucas and his mother? (Answers may include: They knew his name, what he looked like, where he lived, and also his home phone number.)

- Why do you think the bully/bullies made Lucas and his mother targets? (Answers may include: They were easy to find. They were different, ate strange food, and were alone and scared at night.)

Answers

Page 80

1. (a) on the phone
   (b) Max had to identify himself, and Lucas said that it was good to talk to him.

2. They made scary phone calls, put graffiti on the wall, and put awful things in their mailbox.

3. (a) Mom and Lucas were alone in the house and Mom was scared.
   (b) They wouldn't be able to scare Mom as much when Dad was there.

4. (a) They ate different food.
   (b) Teacher check
   (c) Teacher check

Page 81

Teacher check

Supporting Activities

- Role-play one person arguing with another about information and what isn't safe to say in a chat room or on a social networking site.

- Write a letter to Lucas giving him some advice about what he should or shouldn't do about his FACEspace page.

READ ABOUT IT

Hey Lucas, it's Max. How are you doing?

Hey Max. Good to talk to you. But I'm not really great; things haven't been too good around here. We've been having a pretty bad time, in fact.

Sorry to hear that. What's going on?

Well, it's my own stupid fault, me and my big mouth! I went on FACEspace.

FACEspace! Why's that a problem? Most of my friends are on it and like it. They're not having any probs.

Well we have. We've been getting lots of phone calls, some in the middle of the night. When we answer there's no one there. Mom's had some horrible ones when the person at the other end just made spooky noises or said horrible things. The stupid calls at night scare Mom so much. But we don't seem to be getting any calls on the weekends.

I feel sorry for your mom, that's scary.

Yeah, and we've had graffiti on our front wall and horrible stuff put in our mailbox.

What's it all about? Who's doing this and why are they being mean to you? It doesn't make any sense!

Well, I didn't think when I put some stuff up on FACEspace, like my address and phone number.

There's some really mean people out there! But what made them pick on you?

It was probably what I wrote. I talked about Dad being away, and that it made Mom nervous. Then I talked about Mom cooking my favorite foods, how good they are, and what they taste like.

So what's the problem with your favorite food?

Well, I love escargot and I also like to eat frogs' legs. Mom misses lots of things about France.

And you posted all this info on your FACEspace profile for anyone to read? Hasn't anyone told you about cyber safety? Anyway, there are heaps of things you can do to to stop this bullying from even beginning!

FACEspace

Search

Home   Profile   Account

Lucas Wright

Wall   Info   Photos

Edit my Profile

Suggest to friends

Write something about yourself.

Information
Relationship status
Single
Birthday
January 26, 2000
Current City
Boston
Massachusetts
Friends
10 friends

Create a Profile Badge
FACEspace@2010 English(US)

About Me

Basic info	Sex:	Male
	Birthday:	January 26, 2000
	Parents:	Elise Wright
		Gary Wright
	Siblings:	
	Relationship Status:	Single
	Looking for:	Friendship
	Current city:	Boston, Massachusetts
	Hometown:	Boston

Bio — My dad's name is Gary. He is working in NYC and I miss him and my mom, Elise, is kind of scared at night when he's away. Dad only comes home on weekends but the only good thing about it is that when he's away my mom cooks me escargot and frogs' legs when she can find them. They are so good. I could eat them every day. They are really expensive and hard to get but I think they are worth the money.

Work and Education

High School   Fairweather Middle School

Add likes and interests

Contact information

Contact info	E-mail:	lucas@cnect.com
	Cell phone:	617-500-1234
	Home phone:	617-333-2727
	Address:	Beacon Towers
	Windows Live:	lucas wright@bigrigs.com

WRITE ABOUT IT

Record your answers after discussing the text on page 79.

1. (a) How do you think Lucas and Max are having this conversation?

   • **in a chat room**   • **on the phone**   • **in person**   • **by text**

   (b) Explain why you think this.

   _____

   _____

2. What did the bully/bullies do to bully Lucas and his mother?

   _____

   _____

3. (a) What information did the bully/bullies get from FACEspace to explain why they only phoned the house on weeknights?

   _____

   _____

   (b) Why do you think they didn't phone when Dad was there?

   _____

   _____

4. (a) Bullies often pick on people who are different in some way. Explain why they chose Lucas and his mother as targets.

   _____

   _____

   (b) What horrible stuff do you think the bullies might have put in their mailbox?

   _____

   _____

   (c) Write some upsetting graffiti the bully/bullies could have written on the wall.

MORE ABOUT IT

1. If you were setting up a FACEspace page, put a check in one column to show the setting you would choose for the information you wrote for each of these headings.

Heading	Everyone	Friends of friends	Friends only
My status and posts			
Bio and favorite quotations			
Family and relationships			
Photos and videos I'm tagged in			
Religious and political views			
Birthday			
Can comment on posts			
E-mail address			
IM access			
Phone numbers and address			

2. Choose three of the headings from Question 1 and write the information you would put up on your FACEspace entry.

(a) Heading: _____

Your information: _____

_____

_____

_____

(b) Heading: _____

Your information: _____

_____

_____

_____

(c) Heading: _____

Your information: _____

_____

_____

_____

advocate/associate

a person who has not actually observed the bullying, but may suspect it is occurring. An advocate can be very effective in preventing bullying.

anxiety

a state of worry, distress, nervousness, or uneasiness caused by apprehension of danger or misfortune

attachment

a document or file (containing pictures, text, or video) that accompanies a main document or e-mail. Basic plain-text e-mails are unable to transmit most viruses, so attachments are often used to do so. Any unknown, unexpected, or unsolicited attachments should be deleted without being opened.

avatar

a representation of a person online (in virtual reality). An avatar can be a three-dimensional model (used in computer games) or a two-dimensional picture (commonly used on Internet forums and other online communities).

bashing

Internet bashing is a hostile and insulting interaction between Internet users, usually occurring in public forums such as discussion boards, chat rooms, game servers, or websites. Bashing is sometimes referred to as flaming.

blog

a website, or part of a website, created as a "virtual journal" with entries of commentary, descriptions of events, videos, and photos. The word is an amalgamation of *web* and *log*.

bullying

the act of using superior strength or power to intentionally harm, intimidate, or humiliate someone who is weaker

bystander

a person who observes bullying. Bystanders who observe bullying but take no active role in that bullying are themselves classified as bullies if they fail to take any action to stop it.

bystander bully

a bystander who is an accessory to bullying by encouraging a bully by, for example, making statements of support, laughing, jeering, or mimicking

chat facility

see "instant messaging"

chat room

a site on the Internet that allows people in different locations to communicate with each other through typed messages, usually in real time. The discussion may or may not have a moderator.

cyberbullying

the use of the Internet or other electronic communications to bully another person or persons

cyber harassment

a form of cyberbullying in which a bully sends repeated offensive or nasty messages to a target, usually using personal communication channels such as e-mails, texting, and instant messaging

cyber stalking

the use of the Internet or other electronic communications to follow and repeatedly harass and/or threaten another person or group of people, making them fear for their safety

cyberspace

the "invisible world" of the e-mails, computer networks, information resources, and websites that make up the Internet

denigration

a form of cyberbullying in which a person posts, e-mails, or texts information (including digitally altered photos) about another person or other people that is untrue or derogatory

depression

a state of despondency in which a person experiences feelings such as sadness, pessimism, anxiety, helplessness, worthlessness, and guilt

download

to copy data from the Internet to a user's computer, or from one computer to another

e-crime

a form of computer-related crime in which the Internet or computers are used as a medium to commit the crime (also called "cybercrime")

e-mail

messages sent from one person to another (or to groups of people) via computers

emoticon

a representation of a facial expression created by typing a sequence of keyboard characters to indicate an emotion. For example, :-) denotes happiness and :-(denotes unhappiness. The word is a combination of *emotion* and *icon*.

empathy

the ability to perceive, appreciate, and share the thoughts, feelings, or state of another person

exclusion

a form of cyberbullying in which an individual is excluded from a group by being knocked off friend lists, left off party invitations, or not accepted as a friend on social networking sites

filter

a program that processes packets of data (from websites), blocking certain packets and allowing others through, hence restricting or controlling what content a computer user is able to access

firewall
a system that protects a network from unauthorized users, usually for security purposes

flame war
occurs when flaming (see below) develops into a series of heated exchanges repeatedly and personally attacking a person or group

flaming
brief, hostile attacks using offensive language towards a person, group, or institution, usually in public forums such as chat rooms or on websites

game or gaming site
a website that is itself a game, playground, or virtual world. Some games incorporate complex graphics and virtual worlds, where players can chat to and play with other players, while other sites offer single-player games.

hack
to gain unauthorized access to computer systems in order to steal, change, or destroy information

handheld game console
a lightweight, portable electronic device with a screen, controls, and speakers, such as a Nintendo DS™ or a Sony PSP™

handle
a nickname or made-up name an Internet user uses when online

happy slapping
a physical assault on an unsuspecting target, often accompanied by verbal abuse, which is usually photographed or filmed using a cell phone camera. The footage is sometimes sent to others or posted online.

hard copy
a printed copy of data stored on a computer or word processor

hit (Internet)
a request from a web browser for an item from a website. The number of hits made to the web server is sometimes used to measure the popularity of a file or website.

humiliate
to injure a person's dignity, self-esteem, and self-respect by shaming, degrading, or embarrassing them

identity theft/impersonation
a form of cyberbullying in which a bully gains access to another person's (the target's) accounts (or creates accounts using the target's personal information) and communicates inappropriately or rudely with others from that account

instant messaging
real-time text conversations between two or more computer users over the Internet. Often users are only able to chat with one person at a time, although a user may chat with multiple friends simultaneously through separate chat interfaces.

Internet
a vast network of computers (academic, commercial, and government) connected internationally through other, high-speed computers, allowing electronic communication among millions of computers

Internet acronyms
acronyms used on the Internet or cell phones as a method of communication, usually used to save time in preparing messages, such as LOL (laughing out loud) or ROFL (rolling on floor laughing)

Internet forum
See "message board."

intimidate
to intentionally make another person feel fearful or timid

intranet
a private or restricted computer network belonging to an organization that is accessible only to its members/employees or other authorized people

link
a connection between two documents (on the Internet)

login
identifying oneself to a computer system or network for access or use, usually requiring a password

malware
software created to infiltrate, damage, or destroy a computer system, usually without the user's knowledge or permission. Includes viruses, trojan horses, and worms. Malware is short for "malicious software."

message board
a location on a website where users can post (type) messages that other visitors to the site can read and often respond to. A message board (sometimes called a forum) differs from chat rooms in that messages are not shown in real-time.

minority
a group of people who differ (culturally, racially, religiously, or ethnically) from the larger group it is part of

mobile Internet-enabled devices
mobile devices such as phones, laptop computers, and game consoles that are able to access the Internet

netiquette
short for "network etiquette," it is a code of appropriate and courteous online conduct

online forum (newsgroup)
an Internet-based discussion, usually requiring a subscription, in which users can read and reply to others' posts about a particular topic

outing
a form of cyberbullying in which personal or embarrassing information about a person is shared with people the information was never intended to be shared with

peer-to-peer (P2P) networking
a network that allows users direct access to each other's computer hard drives to share files, rather than through a central server or website. Any information in a shared folder (even that of a personal nature) can be accessed and used by anyone using the same P2P software.

phishing
the use of electronic communications to obtain private or sensitive information (such as usernames, passwords, and credit card details). It can be done by masquerading as a trustworthy entity (such as online banks), usually by e-mail or instant messaging.

self-confidence
a measure of a person's belief in his or her own abilities, judgment, or power

self-esteem
a person's sense of his or her own worth; an evaluation encompassing beliefs and emotions, including pride and shame

server
a computer and/or program that holds large amounts of information for one or more websites and streams it to users when requested via a network

sexting
the act of sending or receiving sexually explicit messages, videos, or photos electronically, usually between cell phones

social networking site
a website (or service) designed to build social networks among people, allowing them to communicate and share ideas, activities, events, and interests. Users usually have a profile or other representation with some personal details and social information.

spam
unwanted e-mail, especially commercial or advertising material, sent in bulk to many recipients

spyware
software installed on a computer without the user's knowledge that collects pieces of information about the user(s) and sends it back to another source. Spyware can also take partial control of the user's computer and can be difficult to detect.

tag (social networking)
to attach the name of a friend to a picture or video on a social networking site, so that person and his or her friends receive a link to the picture or video

target
a person who is the subject of bullying

trickery
a form of cyberbullying in which a person is tricked into revealing personal or private information about themselves, which is then shared with others

trojan/trojan horse
computer software that appears to perform a desirable function but actually performs another, such as transmitting a virus

troll
a person who posts controversial, inflammatory, or off-topic messages in an online forum or chat room with the intention of aggravating, offending, or baiting other users into an emotional response

upload
to transfer or copy a file or other information from a computer to a larger system, such as from a personal computer to a network (for example, posting a video on YouTube™)

URL
the address of a web page or resource on the Internet. It is an acronym for "uniform resource locator."

video hosting/sharing site
an Internet site that allows users to **upload** (q.v.) and share videos for others to view online

virus
a software program designed to infect, destroy, or interfere with a computer or a computer's software. A virus can copy itself and be transmitted between computers via networks or removable storage (such as CDs and USB drives).

wall
a section of a profile (such as on a social networking site) that acts as a public writing space, where anyone viewing the profile can leave or read messages

web page
a document or page of information on a website on the World Wide Web

website
a collection of interlinked pages, images, and other files available from the same **URL** (q.v.), published on the World Wide Web

wiki
a website that allows users to add and edit content collaboratively